EARLY YEARS
ON THE TRACTOR SEAT

PREFACE

Some of you will realise that parts of my ramblings have appeared in the old Twenty Parts company newsletter. They have also been used in the *Antique Power* magazine published in America. The result of this is that people come and ask me, 'Are these stories really true?' to which I reply, 'Yes, . . . every one of them.' However, I have done no research on dates – trusting my memory. Many people who have crossed my path are not mentioned, and some who have are not too clearly identified. This is simply because my purpose in writing this story is to record 'how it used to be'. Hope you enjoy it.

This is only the beginning of the story and covers the years up to my marriage in 1948. In later years my wonderful family became closely involved in all my enterprises. I spent some time as a tractor demonstrator for an International Harvester dealer. I also worked with Ford Tractors and with Roadless Traction, as well as importing tractor equipment, and we all helped in putting together our own tractor. In my spare time I produced the *Fordson Tractor Magazine* and vintage tractor *Spare Parts*.

ARTHUR BATTELLE

*This book is dedicated to all tractormen
who have suffered exposure to the elements and the trials of
temperamental machines, but have enjoyed the
contentment of a job well done.*

1

IT occurred to me that some of the memories of almost a lifetime spent with tractors should be set down on paper, in case they might offer amusement, and perhaps instruction, to anyone who has time to read such ramblings. So here goes, as memories of my early years on the tractor seat hit the press for the first time.

My story, like most, must start at the beginning at a time when I had little to do with 'proper' tractors. My tale starts in 1937, when I was 12, during a period when the value of every (old) penny had to be considered before it was spent. Those were days of seemingly endless sunshine or snow, according to the season, when petrol cost 6½d a gallon, potatoes 15d a cwt bag and the weekly wages for a farm worker were around £2.

My first experience of a 'tractor' of sorts was the outcome of a visit to a farm sale with Charlie, the farmer who lived across the road from us. Charlie had a farm of 30 acres and in those hard days over 50 years ago, when the milk cheque was so important to the economy of a small farm, everything revolved around the cow. Charlie had 15 to 20 cows in milk, according to the season, and was contracted to provide 30 to 40 gallons of milk each day: more than this probably meant that it had to be disposed of at as little as 2 or 3 pence a gallon; less than this quota meant that a penalty would be incurred. The cows were fetched in around 5:30 am during the summer months. Milking was, of course, done by hand twice each day, every day of the year.

Once milking was under way Charlie's wife would

light the fire and make the first brew of the day. Winter and summer, the tea would be carried out to her husband in the cowshed. After the morning tea Charlie would continue the (to me) finger-paralysing job of milking. Meanwhile his wife would set up the milk cooler and carry the milk to the farm dairy, filling the 17 gallon milk churn to near capacity with cooled and filtered milk.

At 7:30 am milking was finished and the cows were turned out as quickly as possible to avoid having a whole shed full of manure. In summer Charlie reckoned he could use his energy much more profitably than wheeling barrow-loads of sloppy green cow muck about. After milking the utensils were rinsed ready for their after breakfast wash and sterilisation. The morning ritual of measuring the milk would then take place. The churns had a brass disc with a scribe mark across at each gallon mark. Charlie would carefully add or take out milk until the measure was exact and record the amount in the diary. Then he would roll the churns out to the roadside ready for the milk lorry to collect, usually around 8:00 am.

The day of the sale dawned – at this time such a trip was a real treat, as on a small farm like Charlie's, there was no such thing as a holiday or even a day off. After breakfast the usual jobs were done: the cowsheds were cleaned out, pigs and poultry fed, Doll (our horse) caught and harnessed and the trap prepared. Now all was ready for the journey. Six miles were trotted gently away, there being few cars on our country roads, but care was taken to cross the railway bridge between trains so that Doll would not take fright at a steaming and roaring monster passing beneath her feet. Upon arrival at the sale field Doll was tied to a carefully selected piece of hedge and given a nosebag. Thus all was ready for inspection of the goods on offer.

Set out in lines across the fields was the accumulation of a lifetime's farming: a pile of empty, dented oil drums, green and rotten harness, cart wheels – rotten of course – spanners with rounded corners, an open-crank engine of unknown parentage, root pulper, cake breaker, harrows, mowing machine, swathe turner, carts and waggons.

Walking into the farmyard one saw the animals, each with a number stuck to its rear end, awaiting purchase and transportation to a new home – lifelong friendships broken never to be renewed again. Would the new owner be a good man? Would they just be slaughtered tomorrow? What did the farmer feel looking at his possessions for the last time? A heartbreaking day for him, especially so, when he knew that his business had failed.

The auctioneer took his place by the pile of old oil cans and rang his bell to attract the crowd, including of course the usual itinerant scrap dealer who seemed to start all bidding at the standard price 'Penny mester'. The sale went briskly on, the open-crank engine, bought by the incoming farmer, making 12s 6d (years later I bought that same engine, a Bamford corn-mill and saw bench, for £5). A hay waggon made £1, a horse plough 2s 6d. At the end of the line stood the farm car, an Austin 12 made in 1926.

'Now Gentlemen, what am I bid for the car? Not been used for six months [six years might have been more accurate]. Ran here under its own power. What shall we say, £30 . . . £25 then. Right, start me somewhere. Carry you to market for years. Right sir, ten shillings it is (from the scrap man). £1 . . . now you're out on my right, £1 4s . . . £1 10s . . .' The bidding reached £2 10s and Charlie was the owner of what the auctioneer laughingly called a fine Austin car.

The car, navy blue with real leather upholstery, had

The old Austin car
(Drawing provided by Antique Power Magazine from a photograph provided by the author)

four milk churns sitting primly on the back seat, which in fact had started Charlie bidding in the first place. The next problem was to get it home, even before that, to start it. It had no battery and the starter dogs were so worn that the handle would not turn the engine. This combination of worn-out handle and solid dumb irons between which the handle was located was the best designed remover of flesh and skin ever invented. After a few weeks it seemed most of the male population of our village had scarred hands – usually the right one. On the sale field the ex-owner of the car was consulted, and he agreed to start it, saying it always started first time, but you needed to push it. He usually pushed from the driver's side and jumped aboard when it was rolling, hit second gear and off it would go, providing one had previously set the hand throttle and ignition lever on the steering column. This system would not work on the field, so a group was assembled to push, and sure enough off it went and the driver climbed out of the car for the last time.

At this stage Charlie had had some experience as a motor cyclist though not a lot as a car driver; he happily set off for home not knowing how much petrol was in the tank. He had never driven a car with a gate-change gearbox, nor for that matter had he any documents, licence or insurance – but those were happy, carefree days.

At home the car was parked on a slight slope ready for an instant start. It was always a challenge to park the old car in a position where it could be started. Nevertheless we all loved it – headlamps with brass rims, nickel-plated radiator with the famous Austin winged wheel emblazoned on the front, black radiator cap with finger grips around its rim. The deadly starting handle between the two dumb irons supported the leather-wrapped and jacketed springs, the wings curved over the 21-inch artillery wheels and continued alongside the body to form running boards covered with rubber matting and edged with metal strip. Extra pieces of patterned rubber were placed by each door. These rather small doors had nickel-plated handles reminiscent of railway trains; when the doors were pushed shut there was a satisfactory clunk.

The rounded back to the car's fine coach-built body was topped by the hood. This hilarious structure of stays, pins, rivets and bent iron with bits of canvas flapping about appeared to me to have been invented by someone with a severe and permanent hangover. Seat belts were not, of course, heard of in those happy days, but a suit of armour might have been useful when erecting the hood. Taking the driving seat one was faced with a thick steering wheel carrying the advance and retard lever and also the hand throttle. The instruments on the dashboard were silver rimmed, and the speedometer, reading up to 60 mph, showed 25,000 miles. The car also had a gate-change gear lever, transmission handbrake, the usual three pedals and a petrol filler cap located under the driver's seat. This then was the vehicle we brought back to the farm and which would in due course take over the mowing, haymaking, muck carting etc – the work that old Doll had been doing. She was due for semi-retirement but could on no account be disposed off for she was almost a member of the family.

The old Austin now became a fully fledged working member of the farm staff. Charlie, in his hunger for land, had gradually taken over the village allotments as they became available until he had about three acres of ploughland. This was ploughed and cultivated by a neighbour, and the old car was to ridge the field and cart the manure to set in the ridges.

The day of ridging dawned and we push-started the Austin, having attached a drawbar to its rear luggage rack. This bar had a centre hole to pull a trailer and two holes, one at either end, which we thought would be about right for the ridger. Having already obtained a certificate of exemption from the road tax, limiting the vehicle to a maximum of six miles in any one week on the public road, and third party insurance for the princely sum of 7s 6d a year, all was now ready for the first legal journey on the road.

The horse ridger was loaded into the back of the car with an assortment of old chains and a blacksmith anvil for extra weight. Many problems now became apparent: the inability of the driver to keep straight, the lack of traction from car tyres, the choking poisonous fumes from the rear exhaust blowing into the face of the man who was at the handles of the towed ridge plough. On top of all this was the impossibility of restarting the car if it stalled in the field, with only two men and an assortment of kids to push it. By the afternoon ten curved ridges had been drawn. As Charlie said, they had to be curved because they were too long to fit in the field if straight!

The car had accidentally been stopped and two hours were lost whilst the starter dog was removed and taken to the local blacksmith for modification. This would now start the engine but was only used in cases of emergency as it was not now as hard as it should be. So normally the car was still push started. The plough hitch point had finally been set and various types of skid chain fabricated to provide grip to the rear tyres. At the end of the day the ploughman retired to bed, coughing and being sick in turn, complaining that when he had the horse no one expected him to eat the animal's exhaust even though he thought it would have done him less harm than the car. It was two days before he recovered enough to continue the ridging.

The car exhaust was disconnected and diverted to discharge on the nearside, no silencer being used so it now had a much more 'tractor' sound. Two extra wheels with tyres had been obtained from a car breaker for 10s. The tyres were deflated, wrapped with old harness leather and fitted with old horse shoes in four places before being inflated again. Thus, a pair of 'lug wheels' was made available, to be fitted in the field. From this day forward the car never had more than two wheel nuts on either of the rear wheels.

The ridging was finished with the help of various kids riding in the back of the car and relaying messages between the ploughman and driver. The next operation was to spread muck into the bottom of the ridges that had been drawn. Now the car became a haulage unit. An ex-London Midland and Scottish railway dray on four sturdy ironbound wheels was already resident on the farm, so a drawbar was constructed to replace the shafts, and a good muck-carting unit was now available. The foot brakes of the car were almost non-existent by this time, something to do with the dust from the ridging operation, I believe. But the transmission brake was a gem, locking the rear wheels any time the driver wanted to do so. This was not, however, very productive because the car always seemed to end up crosswise on the road with the dray at some other angle and a generous coating of muck supplementing the tarmac surface. This problem was greatly helped by filling the rear seat of the car with about half a ton of greenish-yellow wet muck. Braking was considerably improved but the leather upholstery was definitely deteriorating. The driver was also learning to anticipate hazards ahead, always being aware of obstruction as much as half a mile away. If only today's drivers were as long-sighted as this.

We made some more adjustments to the Austin: fuel was now delivered to the carburettor by rubber hose – no one could ever keep the fuel line clear for long – and the rear of the car body was cut away and a platform body built in its place. Considerable skill had been learned in using the machine, and the farm now had a general 'tractor' doing a good job. It was so for about the next four years.

I was coming to the end of my schooldays and decided to get a 'real' job rather than just helping Charlie out. Due to illness I did not start school until I was eight years old. Consequently they were not the happiest days of my life, and in fact I refused to go any more after about 13 years of age.

Having left school I obtained a job in a garage about six miles away from home with a wonderful man, Harry Holmes. There were no other staff. I began to feel life was at last worth living although, of course, I had to do all the unpleasant jobs like washing parts and sweeping the floor (which I was supposed to do before Harry arrived in the morning). I also served petrol when it was raining – Harry did it in fine weather so he could talk to the customers. I became quite expert at crawling about on the greasy floor lubricating old cars and holding parts or bolts whilst Harry worked in the more congenial topside position. I also had fun shunting customers' cars around in the garage (without their knowledge of course) or cycling out to help start people's cars.

2

DURING 1940 the milk trade must have improved a little, or maybe the government were looking ahead to the forthcoming war – for I arrived home from work one day to find that Charlie had bought a tractor. I mean a *proper* tractor – a Fordson model F. Things were definitely looking up. I had driven a Fordson on rare occasions so was not without a little know-how, but I had never seen a Model F before, as even in 1940 this was a pensioner of a tractor. Looking back, I think this was probably the day I decided that the bike ride to the garage was too long and I ought to work nearer home. Anyway Charlie, rushing across the yard with a milking machine unit, another sign of increasing prosperity, shouted to me to see if I could put the new arrival in the shed. Great, I thought, and looking it over, setting the controls as I hoped they should be, I went to the handle – it had no ferrule and was covered in the brightest orange paint you would ever see. In fact everything was orange: plugs, flat fan belt, magneto, wheels – everything. I had heard stories of how these old Fordsons could kick so I turned the engine with care, probably too much care – nothing happened. A little more fiddling, more turning and I was rewarded with a few flat explosions and clouds of white smoke. Next time, I said to myself. Another violent swing and the engine was running, downswept exhaust emitting bursts of smoke. Shutting down the throttle to ease the load on my ears, I obtained a steady tickover, most cylinders firing but in what appeared to be random order. As I sat on the seat and looked forward, the radiator

10

seemed to bob up and down in time with the engine: steel wheels, I hear you say – yes they were, and the rear ones had new spade lugs fitted. They rotated within about 18 inches of the body – no wings, of course, on this tractor.

Pressing the clutch pedal I attempted to select reverse gear. This proved quite difficult – not at all what I expected, just a noise like a circular saw cutting granite and a marked drop in engine revs. Try again, I said to myself. More force produced a metallic clank and the engine remained silent. I started it up again and selected reverse with more authority and revs than last time. All was ready to reverse into the shed – my first drive, all of 15 feet!

Letting in the clutch produced a rocking motion of the seat which I now found to be loose. This did nothing for clutch control and the beast took off in reverse, spade lugs clattering on the stone yard, my head clattering on the shed roof and jamming down on to the steering wheel. At the same time my right elbow fouled the spade lug wheel and a heavy thump signified that the rear wall had been reached. With what I considered superb reaction I pressed the clutch, but with the loose seat and excitement my foot slipped off the pedal – I removed some skin from my shin and caused the spade lugs to dig loose earth from the floor and cut two neat grooves in the brick wall. I often wonder now how many people have studied these grooves and speculated on their purpose.

The day after my misadventure we decided to try Henry out on some fieldwork – all Fordsons were nick-named Henry. This meant using the old horse 'scuffler', more commonly called a cultivator. Anyway, it was a horse-drawn implement with five tines and two large wheels at the back. There was another wheel at the front

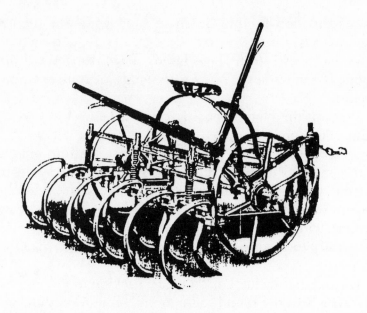

Ransomes scuffler. The one we used was, however, of Howard make

to adjust the height of the drawbar so that the line of draught could be changed to suit various sizes of horse.

What a day that was, working with the Fordson for the very first time. The oil was checked, and fuel poured in. We used petrol for starting up, and paraffin as the main fuel. I can still feel the cold paraffin running down my leg as we tried to fill the tank without using a funnel. Later we bought one, but not before we had removed some of the thick layer of paint some poor misguided mechanic had applied all over the tractor. He had probably used a hosepipe with his thumb over the end in a vain attempt to spray the bright orange colour and make believe the old tractor was much younger than it really was.

After much swinging on the starting handle and some

strong words the old girl started, and along with quantities of blue smoke she was ejected out of the shed. I say 'ejected' because that is exactly what happened: after the gearbox had received its usual abuse and sufficient revs had been produced from the engine to avoid stalling, the clutch was engaged and with a scrunching of spade lugs into the gravel the old thing sprang from its lair. As the Fordson stood in the farmyard, nose gently nodding, the usual smoke being emitted by the downswept exhaust pipe, it looked to us a fine and businesslike machine. The orange paintwork shone. The engine wasn't firing too regularly, but the noise was evened out by the regular click-clack of the two joins in the flat fan belt hitting the pulleys.

We reversed the Fordson up to the scuffler and connected it using a short chain. Charlie took the front and I sat on the implement seat. We were all set to go. Across the home field we went, the scuffler roughly following the tractor, zig-zagging from side to side as far as it was allowed to by the length of chain. I clung on to the lever used for lowering the tines into the ground and contemplated the amount of money that I might have paid for a ride that would have been no more stimulating at a fairground. Halfway across the field Charlie stopped, almost pitching me off the seat, and ran round to the fuel tap: we had forgotten to switch from costly petrol to paraffin. In our excitement at using the tractor we had overlooked the first priority of those not so well-off days: conserve your capital - in this case expensive petrol.

After turning over to paraffin the engine seemed to run much better and the smoke turned a darker blue. We finished the journey across the grass field and came to the road, which we had to travel along for about 100 yards before we came to the gate leading to our plough field. A quick look up and down the road told us that the local policeman was not approaching on his bike, so we took the plunge and drove the tractor on to the tarmac. The result was the quick realisation that spade lugs and tarmac should definitely be kept apart. The whole tractor juddered and the lugs made peculiar perforations in the road; it looked almost as if we might tear a strip off the surface like a strip of stamps. Halfway along the road a cloud of steam enveloped the tractor. This added considerably to the normal amount of steam that spilled from the radiator cap (owing to it having no gasket fitted), condensed and ran down the radiator header tank and blew back into the driver's face. We found that the centre of the water drain tap had fallen out, due no doubt to the heavy vibration of running down the road. Although we found the missing part of the tap, we had no water left, so two crestfallen tractormen made their way home on foot for further supplies.

With new cooling water in the radiator we were ready to start the fieldwork. A small field of about one and a half acres was covered several times in the next three hours. I shall forever remember the smell of the paraffin exhaust and of unburnt fuel leaking from the pipe and dripping on to an almost red-hot exhaust manifold. Just once more over the field and we would have a good tilth to set potatoes in. So off we went for the final pass.

After we had covered half the field, a whistling noise became evident and a new vibration was felt. What could it be? In our ignorance we decided it must be a leak in the exhaust system, so we carried on with our work. The whistle became louder and the engine note deepened. Charlie pressed the clutch, shutting down the engine which promptly stopped. I went to turn the handle to restart the machine – it was firmly stuck and quite immovable.

14

Again we walked home, and consulted a neighbour who was more tractorwise than we were. He had a look at the Fordson and the diagnosis was simple – there was no oil in the sump. The whistling noise had been gas rushing past dry pistons. 'But it was full when we started,' was our cry. 'Maybe,' said our neighbour 'but it ain't now.' So back we went to the farm for oil – in fact another two and a half gallons of it. We took the tractor home and lay in wait for the salesman who had sold it to Charlie. He, wise man, never came near. So, via a neighbour's telephone a sharp message was given to the Fordson dealer who had supplied it. Two days later a truck appeared and carried the tractor away.

A week later the tractor reappeared with more orange paint on it and the assurance: 'It will be okay now.' Charlie had by this time purchased a plough – a brand new one after the experience of the used tractor. It was manufactured by the International Harvester Company of Chicago.

With the tractor back home, it was decided to plough a three acre field just acquired from a neighbour. So off we went once more with our tractor, and this time a new plough as well. The only experience of ploughing belonged to Charlie, and this was somewhat limited being based on a horse plough and the old Austin car. So with this limited knowledge we started to set our new plough and turn over the field. It took two and a half days, between milking, half a tank of fuel and many strange words not found in the dictionary before we felt that we were doing a reasonable job.

We began to feel quite pleased with ourselves. Half an acre later the exhaust note deepened – a hard patch, Charlie said, but soon the tractor started to boil violently. It misfired a few times and then stopped with a final backfire. We rushed to turn the handle, fully expecting it to be stuck, but it turned easily. Two hours later we had cleaned the plugs and magneto points and removed the fuel tank to rinse it out, but all we got from the engine was a spasmodic backfire.

I suddenly realised we should check the timing on the tractor (my experience at the garage helped here). We couldn't see how it could be wrong. But wrong it was. So I reset the magneto and the tractor started right away. My hat size increased considerably and off we went again.

Two rounds later it happened again – maybe I hadn't tightened the magneto up enough. In our rush to retime the engine I dropped a plug terminal down a plug hole. Hat size now considerably reduced, a council of war decided we must remove the cylinder head to get the plug terminal out. I have since done the same thing and left the terminal in the cylinder to get out as best it could, without any problem, but at this time caution and inexperience led us to remove the head. Half a day later the timing slipped again. We found that the worm and

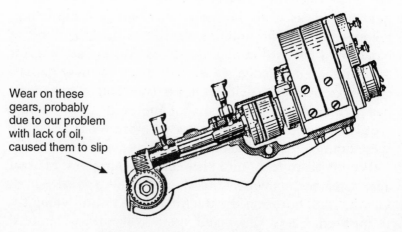

Wear on these gears, probably due to our problem with lack of oil, caused them to slip

Magneto conversion similar to ours

16

wheel driving the magneto was badly worn, probably due to running short of oil. Once again the dealer's truck came and took our tractor away.

I never drove the Fordson again as Charlie's employee. The fact that he was increasing his milk output and that I hated cows combined with my developing appetite for tractor work to send me to a new job. However, on the rare occasions when I had any spare time, I gave him a hand starting the 'beast'.

My new job was on a much bigger farm, run by a man called Hollins whom I called 'Boss'. He was a fine self-made man who taught me a great deal. The war had just begun and most things were in turmoil, so I guess I was employed as a safety valve in case some of the farm employees had to go for military or industrial service – remember the Boss had seen what had happened in the First World War and I was not of military age.

Looking back I now realise the old Fordson was something of a hybrid: it had spade lug wheels instead of cleats, a Model N manifold, magneto conversion in place of the trembler coil ignition and an N fuel tank and radiator – such was the state of agriculture in late 1939. No doubt the tractor had been recovered from the scrap heap to serve in another war.

I smile now when I think of our gloom because the Fordson used two and a half gallons of oil in three and a half hours. The cost appalled us – a five gallon drum of oil cost £1 5s, petrol 1s 4d a gallon and paraffin 4d a gallon. Ploughing cost 15s an acre and I soon realised that a fortune was there for the taking if I could get a tractor. There was plenty of work around and I figured it would be possible to plough at least four acres a day giving an unheard of income of £3 per day (my wages from Charlie had been £1 5s a week).

After my experiences with the Fordson and the decision to move employment to a larger farm I became more involved with bigger and better tractors – Internationals. Luckily, I was still able to help Charlie with the Model F when I wasn't at work.

After the Fordson had been on Charlie's farm for a few months it became more and more difficult to get going, and quite often I was called to help. Charlie would leave a message with my mother asking if I could go over that evening. I would have a good idea what the problem was, and take a plug spanner and a right-hand glove with me. We usually followed the same procedure. After removing the plugs and cleaning them, we poured some petrol into a tin lid we had saved for the purpose, put the plugs into it and set them alight. Whilst they gently burned we checked the fuel and cleaned the vaporiser plate. Sometimes we cleaned the magneto points and swung the engine over without plugs or fuel to make sure no trace of previous unburned fuel was present. Then we put in the warm plugs, and swung the engine over again. Usually the tractor went quite well, for a few days at least.

Occasionally I would drive the Fordson at weekends, usually for a ploughing job on one of Charlie's neighbour's fields. Sometimes in the morning we encountered a starting problem, which was often associated with too much fuel in the engine and not enough spark. We found that a quick way to dry out the engine was to remove the sparking plugs and hold a lighted match just into the plug hole. The result was a loud explosion and, if you got your fingers in the wrong place, sore finger-ends for the next few days. But we did usually get started quite quickly. Do not try this procedure, however, as it is dangerous! I can quote the experience of a farmer (the same man who showed us how to do it) who lived about two miles away.

He had a Fordson F which was older than Charlie's and had ladder sides to its radiator.

On this occasion our friend held the match to the plug hole, got the usual explosion and sheet of flame, but had not wiped the fuel tank properly after filling it. A piece of rag stuffed into the filler hole (there was no proper cap) caught fire and burned fiercely. The fuel tank also burned strongly on the outside because it was encrusted in oily soot and black carbon. Batting the flames with an old sack only resulted in dislodging the rag bung, which promptly set the straw alight on the floor under the tractor. The sump started to burn. By now the fire outside the fuel tank had produced quite a lot of heat and the filler hole which had at first been gently plopping flames out began to burn strongly. At this, our friend decided discretion was the better part of valour and ran away.

Watching from a distance, and no doubt abandoning any hope of his tractor's future, he found to his amazement that the external fires gradually petered out. The fuel tank persisted in imitating a blow torch, but finally there was a kind of soft 'whoof', a sheet of flame shot high in the air and the fire suddenly died. Venturing back to the tractor he found that he was the owner of a Fordson F with oval fuel tank ends and a squarish middle section, but it didn't leak! Amazingly, after a day or so's repair the tractor was again pulling its Oliver two-bottom plough through the farm's awful sticky soil.

We had many misadventures with our Fordson but nothing quite as desperate as that fire. One day after I had ploughed until almost dark, curiosity got the better of me and I decided to see if I could at last move Henry Ford in top gear. Until then we had never managed to get more than a few laboured yards before the engine stalled. This day I found that one of the fields I had to cross on the way back to the farm was downhill. We never worried about the spade lugs perforating the grassland, reckoning these would do it good if we used a different track each day. So selecting top gear, revving the engine hard and slipping the clutch, I managed to get the old thing rolling. What a thrill. With the engine gradually building up revs, off we went down the slope. Now I found just how difficult an F was to steer at speed. The wear on the steering gear meant we took a meandering track, and after a little while, as speed built up, great clods of earth flew off the spade lugs, high in the air. The ones that were not flying straight up were tending to hit me – oh for a camera to catch the expression on my face! After the slipping of the clutch to get the tractor moving in top gear, it never worked properly again. We had to tie the pedal down each night or it was not possible to get the tractor into gear next morning until the oil was warm.

The last time I drove Henry I found that among its many problems due to age was a badly worn hand throttle. This meant that when approaching the end of a furrow, one had to pull the trip rope to lift the plough and shut the hand throttle (which didn't reduce engine revs enough). Then one bent forward and reached around the front of the dashboard to move the throttle rod on that side or else the engine revs increased dramatically as the plough came out of the ground, tending to lift the front wheels into the hedge bottom. At the same time one also had to steer the tractor and avoid the lethal spade lugs. A tall order!

After these experiences I became even more disillusioned with driving a Fordson, especially when compared to the Internationals I was sometimes allowed to drive in my new job. In fact I enjoyed the wider experience of the larger farm, especially since I was not expected to do any milking, and I became the farm mechanic in a small way.

As I look back on these memories it seems amazing that a fifteen-year-old boy would be entrusted with so many jobs, or would even be capable of doing them. But you must remember that the first essential for learning is to be interested in the subject more than the reward that might come from it. The war had just started, and after the first few weeks when our expectations of bombs raining down on us (or worse still, mustard gas – our gas masks went everywhere with us) did not materialise, we began to enjoy the new and exciting life. Money became a little easier. Government controls were either already with us or being talked about. Many men joined the forces voluntarily and conscription was around, meaning people were being parted, sometimes for long periods, sometimes forever. In short, the whole country was in turmoil and, at least to me, it was very exciting.

International Harvester W30. Note the filled in front to the wings.
This feature was added during the depression, when labour was
very expensive, so that women would drive wearing skirts

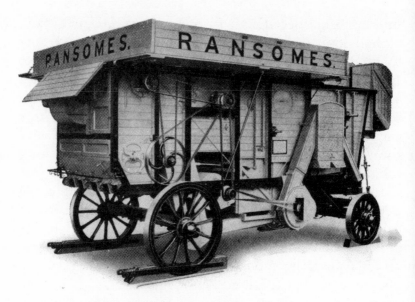

Ransomes threshing machine

Just at this time tractors were fairly easy to obtain. Money was not so easy, however, and many farmers did not have the resources to buy them until much later when they were in short supply. My boss, Mr Hollins, was lucky enough to have the funds to buy a new tractor in 1939: a red International Harvester W30 – quite the best tractor I had been involved with up to that time. The Boss was a very unusual man in so far as he had considerable foresight and was already preparing for a lengthy war. His experience of the First World War had taught him that machinery, and in fact all resources, would in time be very scarce. To this end he already had a wire-tying baler on order, and soon after I came to the farm he ordered a Ransomes threshing drum.

The Boss was a man who had known money shortage. He once told me he drove a bus but the pay was so bad that he borrowed £50 and bought a used tractor and plough (Fordson F of course). Then he took a contract to plough a piece of parkland around a stately home, 100 acres in all, and agreed to do it in two weeks! His wife took his meals to the field, and when he was tired he just slept by the tractor. This was a summertime job, so I guess it was possible to do it.

When the Boss first came to the farm it was full of weeds, as it had been without a tenant during the depression. He had it rent-free for the first year, so the ploughing was done over the summer to clean the land – fallowing we call it. He would take a pair of horses down to the fields at 4 am and plough until he brought the cows up for milking at 6 am. Now, some six or so years later, the farm was a prosperous unit producing milk and cereals.

Haymaking started in late June and the wire-tying baler on order had not yet arrived: I never knew what was said on the telephone but I bet the wires hummed a bit. However, the grass was cut and whilst the farm staff turned it the Boss departed for Liverpool (about 80 miles away) on the W30 to collect the awaited machine. Some delay was experienced, which meant that the return journey was to be made in the dark. The Boss did not worry about small details like that – he bought two cycle lamps, red for the rear and white to adorn the W30 radiator. He arrived home in time for an early breakfast, before towing the new baler down to the fields to start work less than 24 hours after leaving the factory.

Some weeks before this the Boss had been to a farm sale and bought an International 10/20 tractor and a Ransomes three-bottom plough. This was to be regarded as his son's tractor – Sonny as the Boss called him. The tractor was now fitted with a hay-sweep and our harvesting began. It was late June and only a few weeks after the evacuation of the British forces from Dunkirk and this had transformed everyone's attitude to work. I believe we all realised our backs were against the wall and nothing but maximum effort would do.

International Harvester 10/20—open wings

The ploughing of permanent grassland was under way in earnest, much to the disgust of the many dairy farmers in our area. Whilst being pressurised to produce more milk, they were having their best grassland ploughed under directives from the War Agricultural Committees. One of the largest permanent grass fields on our farm was of 25 acres, not large by many standards but big in our area. We called it the corner field, since it was situated at the corner of our village. Sonny was sent to plough it, and after about a week the job was completed. I was fortunate because he was drafted to other jobs and I was sent to disc-harrow the field. I mention this because I can say without question that this was the best and most enjoyable day's tractor driving that I have ever experienced.

The wonderful 10/20 tractor was so different from the old Fordson F – it just plodded on all day in top gear. The sun shone, the tractor was perfect and the resultant seedbed seemed just right for drilling.

Shortly after this news came that the long awaited threshing box was ready and being consigned to Derby, our local town. Soon after it arrived it was commandeered by the War Agricultural Committee (Warag), but not taken away from the farm. This meant that the Boss could not operate in our locality because there was a threshing operator already covering this area.

The Warag had to consider how best to produce the food needed to feed a nation at war and this meant ensuring all requirements could be covered. So if a much needed threshing outfit was operating in an area, in competition with another whilst an area of the county was without threshing cover, then one outfit had to move – ours had to move. There was a financial penalty for this and no compensation could be claimed. The penalty was that out of the £5 per day the farmer paid for the outfit to thresh his crop, the Boss now had to stand the extra cost of travel with its hassle of fuel shortage and the cost of moving his workers the 20 miles each way to operate the machine. There was no specific area laid down but it was strongly suggested that it would not be accepted easily if our outfit moved from that general area leaving crops in the stack waiting to be threshed. As August approached we began to get ready for the threshing season. Little did I know that this was going to be the hardest winter of my life.

Sometime towards the end of that summer we started to prepare for our first outing with the threshing set. Excitement was high. We were due to take up the area allotted to us at the beginning of September, but the Boss intended to thresh some of his own crops before the outfit went away. Corn crops were, of course, cut with a tractor and binder at this time. The Boss, always restless to get on with his work, had the farm running smoothly and crops were usually set early. Thus we were able to harvest as soon as the weather would allow, and so our corn cutting began early in August, and we were ready to try out our new threshing set towards the end of the month.

It took us a whole day to get the machine set to our liking. Later we were to take pride in the fact that we could set up and be running within an hour of arriving on the farm. The International W30 drove the set with magnificent carelessness – it never missed a beat for the two days and only faltered when I, in my inexperience, dropped a wet sheaf into the drum causing a bark of protest from the tractor and a glare from the Boss. My admiration for that tractor grew as we went on.

The Monday morning arrived when we were due to set off to our first custom job. At first all these jobs had been allocated to us by the War Agricultural Committee, but as time went on farmers in that area would come direct to us with requests to thresh their crops. Work was never short – it just went on and on. Leaving home at 6.30 am and returning at around 8 pm, I was just finding out what work was really about. Most of that winter we worked a seven day week. Only at Christmas did we get two days off.

Our first customer was a country landowner who had ploughed up a piece of parkland. It must have been quite a big job for him due to the old oak trees spread around. There were huge numbers of thistles and we threshed for two days in a fog of thistledown whilst my fingers collected thistle spears until I could have screamed. They swelled up and I could hardly get to sleep at night for the

26

irritation. This taught me to pick up a sheaf with the knife used for cutting the string – a bont knife we called it. If one allowed the sheaf to slide down the blade, a slight jerk would both cut the string and distribute the crop fairly evenly over the canvas feeder – all without touching a thistle, one hoped. It is surprising how quickly one learns these self-preservation tips.

I used to tell the man, or Land Girl, passing sheaves to me on top of the drum to give me only one at a time and to pass it up headfirst so I could get it through quickly and thus make the best production possible for the farmer. But often they were too thick or couldn't care less. So I just allowed a pile of sheaves to accumulate until I could see a forkful coming up, and then I would use my knee to push the pile already there off on top of those coming up, smile sweetly and say sorry. The now-disgruntled forkman would have to lift them up all over again. If we got good food and a liberal tea ration from the farmer I would try hard to give him good value for money, but if he was always complaining I used to go just a mite slower – it always paid good dividends to look after the drum-feeder fellow. By the end of the winter I had become a good drum-feeder, being able to slip the crop through quickly and smoothly so giving a nice sample of corn.

Later in the season when labour had got really scarce (it was becoming almost impossible to find a full threshing crew), the War Agricultural Committee were able to provide teams of Land Girls to travel around the farms. They provided a great deal of help in many jobs. On the threshing set we had lots of teams. They used to come for the day, usually in a small pick-up or van, and would build a ladies' area with the first few bales off the machine in the morning. This was usually no more than an L-shaped wall, and if they were lucky they might find a sheet or piece of corrugated iron to cover the corner as a form of roof. These girls were not too concerned about me. I could usually look down on whatever they were doing in their enclosure. If I got too obvious they threw stones at me, but usually we ignored one another. Later still we had crews of German or Italian prisoner of war gangs to assist. They were never any trouble and seemed only too pleased to be involved. Many of them had been country workers in civilian life and were interested in the way we farmed in Britain.

One day when we were some miles away on a contract job I saw a whole tower of smoke rising from the faithful W30. Closer inspection showed that it was coming from the driver's seat area, so I shouted to the Boss and we both ran to see what the problem was. Two days previously we had fitted a winch under the seat, driven from the power-take-off, and yes we had forgotten to fill it up with oil! Much of the paint work had gone by the time we stopped the tractor, as had a bearing. After cooling it with buckets of water we managed to run the rest of the day. The Boss never gave customers money back for stoppages unless they were of desperate length. He rushed off to the nearest telephone to make Sonny aware of our problem and to ring the dealer, who promised to put a bearing in the post for delivery next day. It was surprising that even in wartime everyone was quite sure the parcel would come next morning, as indeed it did.

The next morning I waited for the parcel to arrive, doing odd jobs until it came. I had been thinking what a long ride it would be on my bike to join the others, but the Boss had left instructions for me to go in the van. It was a Morris 8 model which Sonny used around home. He usually drove it with considerable violence, revving the engine until the windows rattled before changing to a higher gear. Nevertheless, it was a good vehicle – about three years old at that time. When the parcel arrived I duly set off on my 24 mile journey. I was 15, certainly not old enough to drive officially, and never having driven on the road in my life before, I learned as I went along. I soon got the hang of it. Such was the way of life in those happy distant days.

3

IN the spring a neighbour wishing to enlarge his farming activities decided to sell his Bedford lorry and the business that went with it. The asking price was £90 and the business was emptying dustbins in an area which covered more than six nearby villages. Having found the local bank manager sympathetic to his request, my father concluded the deal and we were the proud owners of a truck and a bin-emptying round. I was not very keen on this venture but agreed to help as much as I could. It was a contract operation which paid £80 each month. Living on £3 each week, my mother and father paid off the bank and began to produce profits after four months.

The bin job was, of course, most unpleasant: dirty, smelly and, even worse, some of the outlying properties still had outside bucket-type toilets which had to be emptied. The content of these was called night soil because it had to be removed after dark. Do you suppose the local council thought it smelled less after sunset? I can assure them it did not. However, a large coffin-shaped tank was chained to the floor of the truck and the old Bedford toured around the locality with an evil-smelling slurry sloshing about in it. Afterwards the waste was allowed to run away in some farmer's field – all in the needs of fertility.

Even worse were the outdoor toilets *without* buckets. These had a large pit underneath which had to be emptied once a year or so using a wheelbarrow and shovel. I suppose these old outdoor toilets, about 5 ft square and built of good solid brick, must have been extremely strong, thus giving rise to the old saying 'as strong as a brick sh★★ house' often associated with the old tractors.

As early summer came along the threshing set was used less and less until one day we pulled it home to give it a really good service and clean and paint where it needed it. My work with the Boss then began to lessen and I spent more time with my father, emptying bins. We quickly found it was best to take an empty bin into the house yard and tip the contents of the house bin into it, so saving us the return walk with the empty bin. One house on our round owned a small yapping dog. This beast annoyed us so much we always had a spare bin which, as the dog came to meet us, incessantly yapping, we dropped over him, leaving muffled yelps from inside the bin until we had finished that particular house. He usually emerged enraged and covered in household refuse and ashes.

My father, by this time, was fidgeting to buy a tractor

A Fordson tractor, new in 1936, similar to the one we bought, but with cleat wheels rather than spade lugs

so we could start a ploughing contract business. There was much activity in this area due to the ploughing-up campaign to produce extra food for the war effort.

Tractors were, however, quite scarce by now. We eventually spotted a Fordson in a farm sale, but bids went so high we could not afford it. This suggested a visit to our local Fordson dealers, Messrs Gillots of Loughborough, to see if a new one could be obtained. It could not, but for £110 we were offered a used one – a 1936 Water Washer type Fordson. My father decided it was just right for the job, so it was delivered next day, iron wheels and all. How I suffered fitting roadbands over the lugs so we could travel from job to job!

Two furrow International plough with ace type bodies

We now had a tractor. What about a plough? A visit to our local agricultural machinery officer produced one we could hire. This was a two furrow International plough with ace type bodies. The cost of hiring was £10 per year. The plough was new and crated – in fact, identical to the one Charlie had bought to go along with his

Model F tractor. We paid the first year's hire money and left the office under no doubt that we must produce a good work record or our tractor, and its driver, would probably be requisitioned by the Agricultural Committee, which, of course, offered to provide work if we found it difficult to obtain.

Let us look back a little before we start the new and exciting chapter in my life when my father and I owned and operated our own tractor. I have many memories going back to the first house I can remember living in. It was in a village called Lockington, where my father worked on a farm as waggoner (horseman) doing all the ploughing and landwork, feeding the horses before breakfast and making sure they were all right at night – all for £2 a week.

My recollections of Lockington revolve around a three-wheel bicycle which I could ride only when there was no rain: no mudguards meant the spray from the wheels had to be seen to be believed! Friday was the local market day when I was allowed to go into the big farmhouse with the housekeeper and could wander around what I thought a very elegant building and see how the better-off people lived. I did not appreciate what I was learning until some time later. I had the freedom of the farm and could play at will around the buildings and with the men. I can remember taking my father's dinner to the field with Mother, sometimes returning to the farm on horseback. Oh, what modern children miss now we have so many safety regulations. They are so protected that the very rules made for their safety often cause accidents because they have never acquired the basic commonsense that rules and regulations just cannot provide.

This farm provided my first glimpse of a Fordson

tractor. I can remember it standing in its shed very well, but it was never used so I don't think it was here that my passion for tractors was born.

When I was five years old I developed a swelling on my neck which was diagnosed as a tubercular gland; this meant I had to attend the local hospital three times each week for 'sunray' treatment. Whilst this developed my interest in buses and trains, it caused my education to be held back for three years. The fact that I did not go to school until I was eight years old and was obviously three years behind other children probably caused my detestation of the place and my early retirement from that establishment. Luckily I had learned to read. If you can read well, you can learn anything – this was my best achievement at school and has given me much pleasure over the years.

Due to the financial problems of the early thirties the farmer employing my father had to give up his farm. There was a sale and we had to move house taking with us the farm dog who had, for a long time, attached himself to my father. I know not what breed he was, but he was *big* – some sort of shepherd I suppose. At our new house in a village called Thulston, he was the terror of the neighbours, including the coalman. On one occasion we found 'Old Mick' standing in front of the poor man with a paw on each shoulder, defying him to move. Happy days – but not for the coalman!

Whilst at Thulston I became interested in travel, most days tagging along with the horse and float, which was loaded with hay and bags of sweet-smelling corn, to help feed and tend the many sheep the farm supported. I also went around the local villages with the mobile grocer, who had a Trojan van which everyone called rub-a-dub because its split single two-stroke engine made that sort of noise. Four houses and seven years later (when I was twelve) we returned to Ambaston, the village where I was born, and where fifty or so years later I still live. This is where Charlie and the Boss had their farms and where I finally took a shine to tractors, which have ruled my life since the day we returned here.

I have vivid memories of floods in the village. Ambaston, has always been subject to flooding from the river Derwent. The village drainage system originally consisted of a brick culvert running down the street. There was access to this at the end of the village so that water from the brook could be run through it to flush it out. It then emptied into an open ditch which ran through various fields and eventually made its way to the river. This ditch was known as 'sludge dyke'. Unfortunately the level of the brook has, over many years, dropped and it is no longer able to flush out our drains. Of course, we now have a modern drainage system, but at the time I write of this had not been put in, so when we had a flood the brick culvert overflowed, and the drain water ran down the street with the flood. This was not too bad until the water rose to house level, which it often did, and filled one's house with muddy drain-sodden liquid. When the water went down it left a layer of foul mud all over the floors. Little wonder then, that we never had fitted carpets. We recognised it as a big flood when it became necessary to live upstairs and when the water rose to the height at which it put out the kitchen fire. On one occasion it rose so high my father had to remove the electricity plugs from the walls of the downstairs rooms so that the water would not short them out. These floods would visit us most years, sometimes twice a year, but recently with better flood prevention works and a bigger demand from power stations we do not seem to get them.

I have many childhood memories of my grandparents and am lucky enough to be able to remember all four of my grandparents with considerable affection. My father's father originally worked as a coachman and afterwards became a farm manager, then a gardener and latterly worked for our local council. He lived with us for many years and had wonderful tales to tell of days gone by. Suffering from a kind of asthma he would commandeer a half cup of bacon fat from the fried bacon at breakfast time. This he would drink 'for his cough'. As far as I know his arteries did not thicken, nor his heart give up. Anyway, he lived well into his eighties. Granny Battelle, as we called her, was a big, caring lady, mother of four daughters and five sons. I was always welcome at her house, but simply because I lived closer to my other granny I saw more of her and Grandad Hardy.

Granny Hardy used to tell me of the days of her teens when she lived at home. Her father worked in an iron-works in the Black Country and she said, considered himself lucky if he worked three days a week. Granny used to work in a coalyard, weighing coal for domestic supply. It cost half a penny for 28 pounds, and often was bought only at weekends due to the severe financial cramp which was so common in those bad old days. Granny told me that when her father could work three days a week they were relatively well off and could buy a piece of beef for Sunday which would cost eight pence, and could afford a farthing's worth of sawdust to sprinkle on the house floor, which of course in those days was of beaten earth. Little wonder she was a lifelong socialist. She and I disagreed on this point and so decided not to vote in the elections because we cancelled each other out.

Tiring of the Black Country and looking for pastures new, meaning a better life, my gran moved to the country

36

to work 'in service' and that is how she met Grandad, working on a farm. Eventually, when a farm cottage became available, they married, walking to the Church for the ceremony and returning in time for the evening milking. Out of his first week's wages they bought a new pine sideboard and table which lasted all their married life. When my grandmother was in her eighties and in the first house she had ever lived in with an indoor toilet and a bath (she lived there only two years), she asked my mother to help her carry the sideboard and table into the garden and she burnt them saying: 'when I am gone no one will have them.' Sadly, she died a few months later, but is always remembered with love.

4

NOW back to our recently acquired toy – the Fordson tractor. Standing in our yard it really was my pride and joy and how well it started compared to Charlie's Model F. It was not quite authentic as it was not painted the nice Fordson blue of the water air cleaner Fordson, but had been repainted green in 1941 and came complete with a brown radiator blind and a brown sheet with orange Fordson logo on each side. After some time assembling the plough, all was ready to start work. A very brave farmer (or maybe he was just desperate) had agreed to employ us for our first job which was to plough a five acre field. It was about five miles away so with roadbands fitted I proudly drove Henry for the first time. I was not yet, of course, old enough to go on the road (being only 16). Nevertheless, off Henry and I went leaving white marks on the tarmac from the iron wheels. Half a mile down the road the clatter of iron on tarmac changed – the roadbands were loose, and continued to slacken about every half mile of the journey. Much later, with depressed spirits and damaged knuckles, I came within sight of the field. What a relief. Off came the roadbands and on went the lugs that fitted the plough lift wheel.

My father arrived in the car and together we had set the plough by 11 am – we were going strong and were now ready to start our first job as 'cultivation contractors' as we styled ourselves. Later Father left me to get on with the job. How wonderful it was to be working for ourselves on our first contract. Just before dark my father returned. I had ploughed about three and a half acres, my head was singing from the Fordson's vertical exhaust but was I happy and satisfied. Next morning whilst I was finishing the field, two farmers came to see if the job was good enough. Presumably it was because by the end of that day we had 25 acres awaiting us. Our first venture had taken two ploughshares, 20 gallons of paraffin, no oil and some grease. In total, without allowance for wear and tear and driver's time, the job had cost just over £1, and the farmer now owed us £3 15s. These figures always stick in my head just because they were the first.

Now a word or two about our motorcar. It was a Crossley 10, made in Manchester, with a 998cc Coventry Climax engine. The bodywork was an awful light green and black and the roof was fabric. The Crossley had been rescued from the car breaker by Harry Holmes, my boss at the garage. He paid £5 for it and intended to use it himself. It had cost £335 new in 1933 and by 1939 was in the breaker's yard – such was depreciation before the war. Yet it was complete and a runner. In our spare time

The 10 hp saloon in the Quicksilver range. A light four-cylinder car made mainly by hand, top speed 65 mph

at the garage we prepared it for the road, doing a few jobs that seemed necessary. Then the war came along so Harry decided to sell it before petrol rationing came on the scene probably making it unsaleable. He had seen all this in the First World War. My father and I were keen to have a car and Harry unselfishly sold it to us for £7. It ran throughout the war carrying hundreds of gallons of tractor fuel around our locality in support of our contractor business. It usually ran on a mixture of petrol, ether-based upper cylinder lubricant and tractor paraffin. This mixture gave less trouble than the leadfree petrol we were limited to at that time which burned the exhaust valves at regular and frequent intervals. Our Bedford truck also suffered from this terrible petrol and had more valves burned out than the car. Fortunately the valve seats were never damaged unless one ran vehicles too long before effecting repairs. Eventually the government introduced petrol that contained some lead and that cured the valve trouble on the truck. Before the introduction of this new fuel we started to coat the valves with 'Stellite' and this solved the problem.

My second day as a contractor saw me finishing off the ploughing of the five acre field. I then fitted the dreaded roadbands again and started another and larger field. So my life changed again, for the better I believed. For the next few weeks it was plough, plough, plough until we began to get orders for harrowing and drilling. Then it was back to our controller the War Agricultural Committee.

We now hired a Massey Harris Sunshine disc harrow and seed drill for £10 each per year. These of course were subsidised prices. Ownership of the machines was retained by the Warag. This service was provided to help the 'grow more food campaign' which was being pushed so hard by a government needing more and more home-grown food as shipping space for both food imports and war supplies was critically short.

After two or three months of continuous work with our new toy the pace began to tell. I was ready for a change and the Fordson had been getting harder to start each morning, although it ran well once started. Rain finally stopped us working so I spent a day overhauling the equipment. Plugs were well cleaned and the Bosch FU4 magneto had a good check-over, points cleaned etc. This was the first time I had tried to repair a magneto following the instructions and it appeared to have a better spark after my efforts. I was quite thrilled to think I could do something I had not attempted before. The oils were changed and the engine was drained every 50 hours (this is an essential when running on kerosine). So we were ready to start again whenever the weather took up. Having done all I knew how, to improve the morning start situation (part prayer, part curse and part craft), I left the tractor and hoped that the alterations would make it run better.

In the meantime my old boss had brought the threshing set home to do some of his own work and also to try out the new tractor allocated to him by the 'big brother' Warag. The new machine was a Minneapolis Moline, 55 hp fitted with full electrics. This was the first tractor with a self-starter any of us had seen. How we envied the American farmers having such wonderful machinery.

A message was sent to me asking if I could help out for a few days on the thresher. In common with everyone else the Boss was desperate for extra labour and hoped I would feed the thresher as I used to do. I really enjoyed those few days, as Minnie, as we called it, purred away driving the thresher so easily. When the threshing was

A Minneapolis Moline tractor similar to our Minnie

finished the big Dyson ex-road trailer was loaded with 250 lb bags of wheat for delivery to Sowters mill in Derby, our local town. We ended up carrying bags of wheat up a ladder and piling them high in the trailer before the Boss was satisfied with the load. Anyone who has carried one of these bags of wheat will know they are killers on the level ground, never mind up a ladder. We eventually managed 14 tons on our 10 ton trailer.

Minnie had to take the load to town, and so off we went on the six mile journey to the mill. It was on the bank of the river Derwent and had obviously been built there to take advantage of barge traffic which could use the canal network covering the country. At this time it was still fairly complete although very neglected. Leaving home very early we provoked suicidal tendencies in the morning workforce as it rushed to work at the usual last possible minute. But we arrived safely at the mill at about 8 am. The foreman wanted the wheat down the side of the mill. This was reached via a short road just wide enough for a truck, with the river down one side and across the end. Therefore we needed to reverse the trailer alongside the river. I was detailed to do the reversing as I had the reputation of being a good man at manoeuvring four-wheel trailers, due to the experience I had of setting the threshing machine in awkward places. The unit gently moved backwards down the slight slope towards the river. Thanks to Minnie's easy steering I was able to keep the load heading in the direction required until the trailer was near the end of the road and under the hoist for lifting the bags up into the mill. 'OK, stop!' was the cry from my companion. Much to my amazement, disconnecting the clutch with the hand lever and pressing the brake did not stop the rearward motion and the river was only a few feet behind us. We had not noticed a skim of frost on the road so Minnie, wheels locked, gently slid towards the river. A quick swimming lesson for me and a watery grave for Minnie was only avoided at the last moment, when my companion found a brick to put behind the wheel which satisfactorily arrested progress. In spite of the cold morning air I found it possible to sweat even in winter!

Minnie was not quite so lucky about two years later. The Boss had decided to collect a load of ground salt for dressing the pasture, so he and Minnie set off for Cheshire with the Dyson trailer with its rather deep side boards fitted. He obviously misjudged the weight of the salt because the weigh bridge told him there was as much as 20 tons on the trailer. Being a go-ahead gambler by nature he decided to carry on, where a more cautious man would have taken some of the load off. On the journey home he had to negotiate a hill, Weston Bank, down which Minnie began to take charge. The revs mounted and the Boss told me he never felt so helpless in his life. But he stuck to the tractor hoping to make the bottom before he ran out of road or the engine burst. In the event neither happened: the belt pulley which was of the split type and should have been taken off for road work, came undone and with, as he said, a terrifying bang, hit the mudwing taking a vital part of the tractor with it. I believe it was the steering arm but it could have been the brake pedal. Minnie was then firmly in control and broke through a roadside hedge and ended up on her side in a field. Twenty tons of salt was heavily distributed around and the Boss sent sliding across the grass. I often wondered if he swore on that occasion – I had never heard him use bad language in any situation, however disastrous.

After my brief threshing break and the enjoyment of driving Minnie, it was back to our Fordson. This was made worse by the complete failure of my efforts to make it start better. The weather was now dry enough to resume our sowing programme and we needed to sort the starting problem out. A call to our local Fordson dealer,

1936 Water Washer Fordson

Gillots Garage, brought forth the instruction to remove the hexagon brass plug on the choke unit just above the vaporiser plate, and squirt some petrol into it. I protested that the vaporiser plate was already flooding with petrol, but was told, 'We know. But make sure the petrol is squirted down the choke unit and not down the small straight tube into the vaporiser.' The result was that Henry started on the third pull, and that was the way we always started him until I eventually found the trouble. (*See* illustration.)

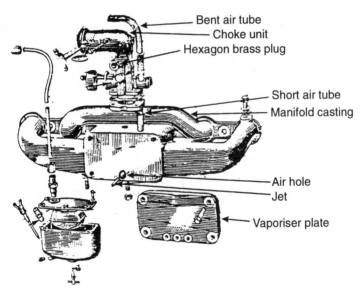

At the base of the bent air tube is a right-angle turn in the manifold casting; this was absolutely solid with carbon and had to be drilled out so that the air, which should have flowed past the jet in the vaporiser plate, could resume its journey and carry the fuel to the engine. The starting problem was due to the lack of this air, but when the tractor was running the suction in the vaporiser plate was so high that air leaks around the plate were enough to take the fuel to the engine.

Fordson engine

The local Warag field officer, Mr Wooliscroft, was making his rounds in our area and persuading or, if necessary, pressurising the local farmers to plough more land, in a never-ceasing attempt to produce more food. Most of our farmers could not easily accept the idea of ploughing ancient pasture on which the locality's history of dairy farming had been built. In addition, they did not have the expertise or the machinery to handle arable farming. New machinery was, by now, difficult to obtain and the few items of used equipment available were extremely expensive. This meant we were in great demand, having most of the tackle and certainly the time to carry out this work, under contract conditions.

Having sorted out which fields to convert to arable, Mr Wooliscroft passed from farm to farm in the parish leaving some very unhappy farmers behind him. They nevertheless knew that to defy the Warag orders left them in danger of being dispossessed and so losing their farms. Of course, if they were no longer farmers and their age was right, they were liable to be drafted straight into the army. This was a harsh and difficult time in Britain. Many of our country people were going to the war. I was not old enough to serve, but seeing all this happening around me and experiencing the air raids and the food rationing coupled with other shortages made one grow up pretty quickly.

On one occasion I was helping Charlie on a Sunday afternoon and had taken a bag of 'chop' and some hay to a few young beasts in a field about half a mile from the village, when the air-raid siren blew. This was not unusual, and my reaction was to ignore it. Having fed the animals I became aware of the drone of a German plane. This characteristic drone was, I believe, caused by the use of fuel injection on their planes, whilst ours had carburettors to feed the engine. Anyway, I stood about 50 yards away from the hedge and looked to the sky hoping to see the raiders. In the next village, Elvaston, there was a battery of anti-aircraft guns and just as I saw the plane, the earth shook as these guns opened fire. I was at least half a mile from the nearest human being and the shattering roar of guns was only a few hundred yards from me – it was just a little scary. I was about to move in the direction of home – you could say run – when I saw the anti-aircraft shells exploding around the plane. This was quite new because usually we had air-raids only at night and I had never seen the puffs of smoke near a plane before. Being intrigued I forgot that what goes up must come down. A few seconds later the scream of falling shrapnel was all around me. Having seen some of the bigger pieces that had fallen during previous raids I realised the danger and to say that the 50 yards to the hedge was covered in Olympic qualifying time is probably an understatement. The plane droned on, the guns fell silent and I 'hurried' back to the village.

The result of Mr Wolliscroft's visits soon became evident. We began to receive many orders to plough grassland. To me this was a wonderful experience: the turf turning over in rubber-like furrows giving off a characteristic smell of mushrooms.

It was during this time that I saw a ghost. We received an order to plough a five acre field of old grassland. The farmer told me that even his grandfather could not remember it ever being ploughed before. It was bordered on three sides with overgrown hedges and on the fourth with a graveyard belonging to St Chad's Church in the small hamlet of Church Wilne. (I was later to be married in the same church, but that is another story.) Maybe the big hedges, churchyard, yew trees and the tips of gravestones

47

just showing over the wall on that fourth side set the active mind of a sixteen-year-old jumping to conclusions. Also we were aware of the nightly air raids and so darkness had a fright factor beyond what was normal.

The pressure to plough more and more acres was increasing and farmers were always coming to see how I was progressing so they could form some idea as to when their turn would come. So even when I finished a field at 3 pm, just before darkness fell in the winter days, there was no let-up in the pressure. An early finish to any of the seven days' weekly work was not acceptable.

The field I was working on had been mowed for hay that year and the haystack stood in the centre. Normally the winter feed would be kept in the stackyard near where it would be required, but during the war it became customary to disperse the stacks around the farm so the risk of fire from bombs etc was lessened and at least some of the winter feed would survive. I parked the car by the stack and hurriedly marked out the field before darkness fell, carrying on with the ploughing until I felt it would be easy to finish the next day and move on to another field before darkness fell yet again. It was a hazy night although moonlit. At about 8 pm I decided I had done enough and could go home. By now we were all getting used to the darkness: under the blackout regulations there were no street lights, no light from the house windows and all vehicle headlights carried masks and frosted glass. So if there was no moon everything was almost invisible. We were all growing carrots in the garden in response to the Ministry of Foods's advice to eat them to aid our 'see in the dark ability'. Parking the tractor by the stack I stopped the engine and covered it with its sheet, which I propped away from the exhaust with a stick carried for the purpose. The silence was almost total after the noise

48

of the engine had ceased. Turning away from the tractor and towards the car, I saw a white figure across the field.

To say I was terrified was the understatement of the year. I went cold and then dived into the car, making sure all the doors were locked. Sitting there I looked at the apparition, feeling sure it was also looking at me. The churchyard was on my left, and a small wood on my right with the figure standing in front of it. I suddenly thought of the car headlights, masked though they were, and turned them on and the figure disappeared . . . turned them off and there it was again. Frightened though I was, my curiosity was aroused. The figure had not moved towards me, so praying the car would start I pulled the choke and pressed the starter – it started. Thanking my lucky stars I again turned on the headlights: the figure promptly disappeared, only to reappear when the lights were turned off.

I saw a white figure standing in the hedge across the field

I could not leave a situation like this even though it was very frightening and I could have driven away through the gate which was, thankfully, open. Instead I slowly drove towards the figure, knowing of course that the doors were safely locked. Switching the lights on and off alternately I saw the figure appearing and disappearing as before. It was not until I came close to the figure that I found what it was. Someone, possibly a gamekeeper or maybe a worker taking a short cut home, had left an almost perfect silhouette in the overgrown hedge and the light sky behind showing through had produced my 'ghost'!

Some time after this adventure the Fordson began to have the usual gear engagement problems. This was something we had never experienced before on our own tractor, only on the old F which belonged to Charlie. However, the weather became very wintry indeed and we decided to tackle the clutch repair whilst the ground was too hard to plough. We had a workshop of sorts but were not really equipped to split a tractor and operate on the clutch. A set of chain block and tackle which we had found at a farm sale was hung up on a convenient beam, which promptly started to sag even before the tractor was attached to it. So two props were cut and wedged into place each side of the tractor to give us what we hoped was the right strength to lift the Fordson. I think here it is necessary to warn you all not to copy some of our rather risky procedures. When I look back over the years and think of some actions I have taken in the past, I wonder how on earth I have survived.

This clutch repair, being the first I had tackled, took me a whole day. Later it became second nature taking no more than half a day: usually a wet afternoon twice a year, was all that was required. Eight months after fitting a new set of clutch plates the tractor would be split again and all plates cleaned free of the carbon build-up. The driven plates which were usually flat by this time would have their ⅛ inch curve bent into them again. On one occasion we rebuilt the clutch with one of the driven plates missing to give extra clearance to ensure easy gear engagement. We never experienced any undue clutch slip from this practice and the clutch did give us an extra four months work before we had to fit a new set of plates. (*See* illustration for clutch layout.)

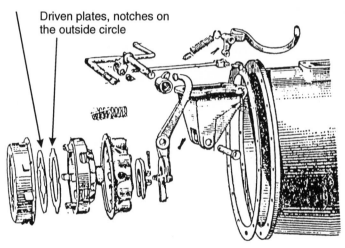

Driving plates, notches on the inside circle

Driven plates, notches on the outside circle

Fordson clutch models F and N

When the Fordson clutch had been repaired the weather was still holding up our work programme, so after servicing the machinery I was able to job around with my former employers, earning a crust as we say. During this period a liver and white springer spaniel, called Bruce, took up residence with us. He belonged to a neighbouring farmer who had quite a number of sheep. Now whether the farmer thought a spaniel would make a good sheepdog I do not know, but Bruce, the spaniel, knew for certain he would not. Treating sheep with great disdain and having nothing to do with them, Bruce won this battle of wits and the farmer gave up trying to train him. Bruce lounged around all day contributing nothing to the well-being of the farm and in consequence became unwanted and a little neglected.

Eventually finding that he obtained more food at our house than at the farm, the dog must have decided to move over, although the farmer became a little miffed at this. Bruce settled in and eventually the farmer decided we had better keep him.

At about this time Charlie took on his cousin, Fred, as a tenant in one of the farm cottages. Fred turned out to be a milking machine fitter, motorcycle enthusiast and gunman – sporting of course, usually for the pot and it was through his interest in Bruce that I made his acquaintance. Bruce, who had taken to sitting at our gate guarding his new home, took a dislike to Fred – we knew as soon as Fred came out of his garden gate, Bruce barking furiously at this figure with a gun walking down the street. After a few days of this Fred called out to me and asked if Bruce was any good as a gun dog. I said probably not; as far as I knew he had never been trained to the gun, but he was certainly the right breed and had a pedigree to prove it. Fred asked if he could try him. Of course I agreed, perhaps having visions of Bruce at last earning his keep by helping our meagre meat ration if the gun and dog could work in accord. The result of this conversation was that Bruce, tied on the end of string, tail between his legs was towed away by Fred to start work. Two hours later they returned, Fred with a big smile, Bruce bouncing along as happy as I had ever seen him, having recovered three mallard ducks off the river. This was the first of many adventures we all had together. Bruce never barked at Fred again — he had found his destiny.

I well remember the frosty winter nights when we all sat under the river bank. Bruce never flinched when a gun went off only inches above his head, and when he had recovered a duck from the river he would sit with water running off him until it froze. Then we had to grumble at him to keep still because the icicles rattled so loudly we were concerned the noise would betray our position. This untrained gun dog was a tremendous help in keeping our meat ration up to reasonable amounts. I believe the official ration was six ounces of meat per person per week at this time. We lived to some extent on wild duck and considered ourselves very lucky. Bruce had his share. The only fault we ever found with him was his love of doing things with as little expenditure of energy as possible. For instance, if we shot a duck and it fell into the river, Bruce would instantly respond and attempt to dive into the river to retrieve it, but when he had it in his mouth he would look carefully at each bank of the river and head for the nearest. If this was our side, we made a fuss of him and all was well, but if the other bank was nearest Bruce would carefully put the bird down and then swim back to us wagging his tail as if to say 'I am clever.' We did not think so at all and quickly learned to hold him back until the bird had drifted nearer to our bank before we released him to fetch it.

5

WINTER began to affect our work in late January and finally we had to turn to trailer work when the ground became too hard to plough. A neighbouring farmer had a large manure heap surrounded by cowsheds. The manure was beginning to dwarf the sheds and yard so we were asked to move it by providing a tractor and driver, paid by the hour. The farmer was to provide the trailer. The best he could provide was a four-wheel dray. This is basically a flat-top vehicle with two axles, one of which swivels to provide steering, and is usually hauled by a horse. This particular vehicle had originally been owned by the railway company for delivery duty. There were many of these pensioned vehicles to be found on farms as they could be bought quite cheaply from the railway depot when a sale took place. This one, in common with many more, had the normal iron-banded wooden wheels, a drawbar in place of the horse's shafts and no side boards to keep the manure on the flat top.

It was normal practice to stack the muck with the most straw in it around the sides and throw the loose into the middle, thus carrying a respectable load. There were two staff, myself and a farm worker, with the cowman helping to load and returning to his cow duties whilst we clattered off to unload. We made heaps at convenient distances, so spreading could be done later. I drove the tractor whilst the farm worker threw off the muck. During one of these trips to unload I met my friend Terry for the first time. He was about 12 at the time and his family had just moved into the village. He asked

54

for a ride and after only two hours or so was doing most of the tractor driving whilst I helped with the unloading to speed matters along. The Fordson was easy to drive, though good judgment was required to navigate the corners on slippery and rutted surfaces. Terry was at just the right age to absorb the safety rules – he was not yet at that grown-up, over-confident stage at which lives can so often be endangered.

I still had considerable contact with Charlie who was now providing some of his milk direct to a farmer in the neighbouring village of Shardlow. I was with him one morning when the van arrived to collect the milk. The previous night we had experienced the worst air raid of the war in our area. Many bombs had fallen on the glass houses in Shardlow and in the surrounding area. The nearest bomb was about half a mile away from our village on the lane leading to Shardlow. The largest bomb had fallen in a hedgerow along this lane and partly blocked the road. The crater was big enough to hold a small house – enormous to us, but no doubt quite small to cities like London or Coventry. This latter city was the target for many of the bombers passing over us and perhaps on this night the glass houses of Shardlow, shining in the moonlight, may have attracted the bomber crews who mistook them for factories. We had spent a semi-terrifying night listening to the heavy crump of bombs and the sharper crack of the anti-aircraft fire. We cringed in our homemade shelter every time we heard the scream of a falling bomb, many of which to our amazement never exploded, comforted by the legend that if a bomb is heading directly towards you its 'scream' will not be heard.

The farmer's van arrived next morning and the driver related tales of the devastation to Shardlow Nurseries and of the bomb crater down the lane. He told us how he had to move some of the dirt thrown out by the bomb before he could get his van past and how, whilst he was moving the dirt, he had seen a set of bomb fins sticking out of the ground near to the crater; deciding they had been blown off he tried to pull them out of the ground for a souvenir, but failed to do so. Later that day the army came and closed the road whilst they removed unexploded bombs – one of which our friend had been trying to take for his souvenir! Ten bombs were eventually exploded or removed, mostly from the crater area and near a small brook which crosses the lane, but we heard more than this fall so I guess there are still some left there. It is very low lying and wet land around the brook and bombs in this type of land will sink over the years to a considerable

Parkin and the bomb fins

depth. In all it was reckoned that 150 bombs fell in and around Shardlow that night without killing or injuring anyone.

A few days after this excitement we were able to resume our fieldwork, and after ploughing and preparing a seedbed for a customer in Draycott I discovered the main disadvantage of the Fordson's water-filled air cleaner. We always drained the water from the tractor engine if we thought there would be a frost, but rarely drained the air cleaner, being in a hurry to get home as there were Home Guard duties to do now the war was reaching a critical stage. This particular night I did not drain the cleaner, so after the frost I found the tractor not running very well. Terry was driving as we drilled a field of spring oats but for some unexplained reason Henry was only just struggling along in bottom gear. This was puzzling me because we had done enough drilling to know that second and sometimes even third gear could be used. Walking alongside the tractor I was experimenting with various fuel needle settings: to my surprise the needle jet had been only one and a half turns open instead of the more usual two and a half turns. Almost unconsciously I pulled off the rubber stopper from the air cleaner: the tractor jumped forward two or three yards and then stopped.

Eventually we found our missing power by propping the air cleaner bung open with a stick taken from the hedge, thus letting the tractor get enough air to operate properly. Later, when time permitted, we dismantled the air cleaner and found that the twin float had sunk and was stopping the air feeding the engine. In addition, I had pumped too much grease into the bottom bearing of the steering column and the air passage feeding the air cleaner was almost blocked. How many water washer Fordsons suffer from this problem, even today, I wonder.

The float had been squashed by the frost and a seam damaged, but I have found that the usual problem with the float is that it rubs on the air cleaner casing and thus develops small holes, over the years, that let in water. This makes the float sink which in turn strangles the tractor's air supply. To repair a float it is first necessary to let out the water. This can be done by drilling an ⅛ inch hole in the bottom. After soldering up the drill hole the float must be submerged in a bucket of warm water thus heating the air inside it which will cause a stream of bubbles to come from where the leak is situated. Solder this up but always look for more leaks before rebuilding the air cleaner.

During this winter we had to find work as best we could. It was okay to do casual work around the farms but this did not produce the amount of money that using our tractor did. In any case we always had the Warag breathing down our necks to keep the tractor productive. They were fond of reminding me that I could be better employed carrying a rifle for the army than letting my tractor stand idle whilst I was doing casual work on farms. I, of course, would ask how many 16-year-olds the army required. After a few well-chosen words had been exchanged by both sides, the agricultural officer would drive away in his government car and I would stamp away on my two feet making some comment about red tape and non-productive agricultural officers. I suppose these exchanges had some effect because I found another use for Henry. This was on our local estate.

We lived on the estate – a tract of land covering our village and several others which were all owned by the Earl of Harrington. He let out farms, various cottages and small agricultural type units. His home was Elvaston Castle, a big house dating back to the seventeen hundreds. He himself was in the army, whilst the castle was occupied by a teacher-training unit evacuated from a more dangerous site in a nearby town. The castle grounds covered some hundreds of acres comprising woodland and parkland, beautifully laid out with neat trimmed hedges and stone statues. There were long drives on the estate, and some of the family's carriages and horse-drawn traps still survived in the coach house in the castle yard. There were, of course, several acres of lawn and much to my amusement, tucked away in a cart shed was the oldest lawn mower I had ever seen – steam driven with a boiler mounted on top.

In days gone by the estate had quite a large staff, mostly local people who lived in houses and cottages belonging to His Lordship. The estate yard had good workshop facilities for blacksmith, joiner, plumber, brickworker and electrician and there was even a sawmill, a saw doctor's surgery with machines for sharpening hand saws, circular saws and band saws, etc., grooms accommodation and stables for riding, carriage and working horses. In short it was almost like a small village. This traditional state of affairs began to crumble during the First World War and by the time the Second War came along most of the staff were gone, either to the army or to more important work. There were no horses for working in the woodland and only three of the more elderly staff were left to provide the estate farmers with timber for repairs and fencing materials for the fields. Thus I found an opportunity to work in the woods with the tractor in place of the long-gone horses.

You will recall that we had already found off-season work carting manure for a local farmer. This had caused us to purchase a pair of pneumatic rear wheels, leaving the front ones in their original cast iron form. We were unable to purchase pneumatic front wheels and tyres because in this time of shortage the iron front wheels could be used on all surfaces, thus little effort was made to produce pneumatic front wheels. Rear wheels, of course, could only be used on the land so there was great urgency to produce rear wheels that could be used on land and road. We got our pneumatic rear wheels from a local tractor dealer who sold used tractors and had a dubious reputation for quality. However, he had found that the local foundry could cast wheels if he provided the amount of scrap iron required. Where he obtained the Goodyear agricultural tyres we did not enquire, but we were able to purchase a pair of wheels and tyres for the outrageous sum of £60. Thus we could look for seasonal work which would expand our tractor usability, and so we came to work on the estate carting fallen trees to the sawmill.

The remaining three estate workers were men who had lived in the village all their lives. Jim Booth was the eldest. He had been in the employ of Elvaston estate since leaving school and at this time was around sixty years of age. He had served in the trenches in France during the First World War and survived to return to the village to retire at seventy-five and live for almost twenty more years, before being buried in the churchyard which was within a short distance of Elvaston Castle. His brother Albert, just a few years younger, acted as part-time gamekeeper and helped out in the woods and with the sawmill. The only other worker was Herbert Madeley, who worked full-time in the woods.

I remember all three of these characters with affection, having spent many hours working and yarning with them. I recall Albert giving me a rabbit he had shot for my dinner. I placed it in a bag in the back of my car and some days later wondered what the crackling noise coming from the rear was – it was a bag of maggots, there being very little left of the rabbit by now. I remember Jim telling me of an unfortunate incident: he was standing by a tree relieving himself when his most vital organ was stung by a wasp. He told me it was the most painful experience of his life – we, of course, thought it hilarious.

This was quite an entertaining period for me because I was now working with people instead of by myself. There was the excitement of discovering a poacher and trying to catch him and also the interesting diversion of finding girls from the training college carrying out assignments with their boyfriends in the woods; many were the embarrassed girls who fled as our tractor approached. I had the interesting experience of cutting down a large tree, which was new to me. Most of the trees we carried to the sawmill had fallen over during previous years. We only cut down trees that were required for special-purpose wood, or those that had reached maturity and were deteriorating.

One memory that stands out from this time is when we were removing a fallen tree that was partly blocking the main drive to the castle. Shortly before, there had been an air raid and a few bombs had been dropped across the grounds, some falling in the lake at the front of the castle. We knew this by the large number of dead fish floating around. A member of the army disposal team who had come to Shardlow told me that usually a certain number of bombs were dropped together – I think it was a stick of six. We knew that three bombs had fallen in pasture land, the shrapnel injuring a cow – which luckily recovered, and we assumed that three others had fallen in the lake.

This morning we took our equipment to recover the

tree and moved the tractor to a patch of rough grass and small bramble nearby, whilst the fallen tree was prepared for its journey to the sawmill. The tractor was never stopped during the day so we did not use petrol to start it again, kerosine being cheap and unrationed. Henry was gently nodding away over to our left. Looking over towards the tractor some time later I noticed the grass and bramble smoking against the downswept exhaust, so taking a hedging hook I cut the rubbish away from around the base of the tractor and then went cold – I was looking at a circular hole in the ground just under the front axle. I knew immediately what it was: one of the bombs we thought had dropped in the lake – it was still live. Here I was, looking down the hole left by it, whilst Henry gently pummelled the vicinity with his iron front wheels.

I backed off and discussed the situation with the others. Deciding that discretion was the better part of valour, we retreated and called the bomb disposal squad. As I walked away I thought about Henry and what it would mean if he were to be destroyed. We did not carry insurance in those days, and would never be able to afford another tractor. 'I'll reverse it off,' I told Jim. 'Duna be daft. Yowl be blowed up,' he said. But I had decided to move Henry, so approaching from the rear (it seemed safer to keep the cast iron body of the tractor between me and the hole, although it would not have made any difference if the bomb had gone off), I gently climbed onto the tractor. Now if you want to practice getting a Fordson smoothly into gear and moving it without revving up the engine, and craftily driving it backwards, try parking it over a live bomb. It does wonders for your driving skills! The bomb disposal team came the next day and dug the offending object out. It was not very deep in the earth because the ground was hard in that place, but they did confirm that it was armed and that the fuse had not been activated for some reason.

The sting in the tale of this story is that twelve years later, when our family was working a farm in the nearby village of Thulston, I was mowing grass when the front wheel of the tractor dropped into a hole. Because I knew the field and that there should not be a hole, I dismounted to inspect. It was round and about two feet deep with grass growing at the bottom. It was awfully familiar, and looking up I realised that it was just in the next field that the cow had been injured by the shrapnel all those years before and that this hole was in line with the ones we knew of. It seems that only one bomb had dropped in the lake and that this was the last remaining missile. The local policeman was told and he came to inspect. 'It cannot be a bomb after all these years,' was his reaction. 'Okay,' I said 'But you had better notify the army; they will know much better than we do.'

A few days later an officer and his driver arrived in a Jeep type vehicle. 'There is something mechanical there but we do not know what or exactly where it is, but keep the cows and tractor away until we come back,' was their verdict. Later they dug down about ten feet, making a hell of a mess in the field, which was at the side of a brook and not well drained. They fiddled about for another two days with various instruments, then confirmed that it was a bomb which was in very deep and had penetrated under the brook into running sand. Their opinion was that it was now harmless and that it would be a civil engineering job to remove it and that it was best to leave it alone. They were not to know, of course, that about 25 years later a whole batch of houses would be built on the site and the brook would feature as an attraction at the

Fishleigh winch

bottom of the gardens. Someone now has an added 'attraction' to their garden that they do not know about.

Winter passed on and the work in the woods continued. We were being paid 8s per hour, and although this now seems a ridiculous amount for a tractor including driver and fuel we were glad enough of the work. Part of the estate woodland had been cleared just before the war and was now overgrown. Clearing this area, about twenty acres, was a fill-in job to do when we were not required to draw timber to the sawmill. It soon became evident that the overgrown blackberry and alder trees were beyond Henry's powers. Luckily, during a visit to the Warag machinery yard, I found a Fishleigh winch which could be hired for 8s a week. I fetched it home and set to work in the woods pulling stumps and clearing the area that the estate hoped to replant in the not-too-distant future. To operate the winch we had to buy a power-take-off unit for the Fordson. Fortunately the tractor was a 4.3 top gear or we could not have fitted this unit. The shaft came out slightly off-centre at the rear just under the right hand axle shaft casing and then connected to the winch via the usual shaft (no guards of course). When

64

operating the winch one was constantly climbing on and off the tractor, trying to avoid the unprotected shaft each time – I still have both legs and arms, and so has Terry who did quite a lot of this work when I was doing small jobs for other people.

6

AS spring came along our contracting workload increased until we had to postpone the estate work. We obtained a set of disc harrows and a mowing machine, so our stock of implements was increasing at the same pace as our work. By this time I was, I hope, becoming a better businessman. I was certainly enjoying the responsibility. I was producing price lists to circulate amongst the farmers and also visiting markets and sales to seek custom. Our truck was still clearing dustbins but also delivering more and more cattle food for our local corn and fodder merchant, F. E. Stevens. This was the result of the increase in agricultural activity and the shortage of labour, which meant that very often the company did not have enough drivers for their own fleet of trucks.

The dustbin job was now finished by Thursday night, leaving the rest of the week to carry fodder around the local farms. It soon became evident that our reputation was growing – many were the farmers who came to visit with cultivation orders, until we were completely over-done with work and it was evident a change of organisation was called for. This was achieved by badgering the head teacher at Terry's school to release him from studies at certain times when the moon was light enough to allow me to drive during the night. This meant I could rest in the day whilst Terry used the tractor. This was quite successful and we managed about an extra week and a half's work out of each month. Quite what his parents thought about this neglect of education I am not sure. But it was not such a high priority as it is today, and later the experience he gained stood him in good stead when he applied for tractor-based employment.

The wildfowling season had finished so our duck dinners were a thing of the past for the time being. Pigeons were still to be had so it was now pigeon pie that provided our extra rations. But a crisis was now looming – a shortage of cartridges for the shotguns. Fred had two guns and I now had one of my own. Fred, of course, was a milking machine fitter and this meant that he had cause to travel quite a lot and so his petrol ration was granted accordingly. Even so, he could not find enough cartridges in the various gunsmiths' shops visited during his travels to keep us in pigeons. Now one of the costs of having a milking machine fitted, at least if it was purchased from the Alfa Laval company, was that the farmer must find board and lodgings for the fitter. So it was that Fred stayed in many differing types of accommodation. He described them as either 'good grub shops' or 'they would not give you the droppings from their nose' places. At one of these farms he found a book about shooting which he believed would solve our cartridge shortage. It gave instructions for filling cartridges and making the gunpowder to load with. We had no problems finding the supplies needed and we also found a pestle and mortar for grinding the ingredients and a machine for curling over the end of the cartridge when it was refilled. We were now saving spent cases ready for our venture into explosives.

Having obtained all the ingredients we required and ground and mixed them, we were ready to try loading. We already had a good supply of percussion caps, which were not difficult to get hold of, probably because the gunpowder to use with them was not available. We removed a spent cap from an old cartridge and carefully fitted a new one, being certain to press it into the cartridge case using only the outer edge to avoid prematurely exploding it. We weighed the powder and poured it into the case. Next a felt wad was cut from an old piece of underfelt which was then well tamped down with paper. The specified amount of no. 5 shot was poured in, tamped down, and the top of the cartridge turned over with our machine. Later we became more particular and heavily varnished the turned-in cartridge end to give it a better explosive value. Now we were ready for our first trial.

All this experimenting had to be done at night as we were both working in the daytime and I was also busy on moonlit nights. However, we managed to find time for a trial. A cartridge was placed into the twelve-bore breech, and fired. The effect was surprising – a vivid flash and bang was followed by a cloud of smoke and bits of burning paper gently descending from space. I guess our position was visible from half a mile away, probably more for a bird on the wing. Anyway we decided to try out six each on our next pigeon shoot. We were disappointed – the pigeons remained unharmed and we had no pigeon pie.

Reading further into the book we found a test procedure listed. It recommended that two sheets of newspaper should be fastened to a board and marked in the centre as a target. We had no board that was big enough but Fred soon solved this problem by proposing that we use the 'petty' door. This was his name for the little brick-house toilet at the bottom of the garden. Making sure nobody was sitting inside, we promptly put the building out of bounds for the duration of our test and two sheets of newspaper were fastened to the door. The book told us to fire a known quality cartridge at one piece of newspaper, to set up a control. This we did using a no. 5 Eley. Comparing the result with that using our own cartridges the problem was easily seen – our shot only just reached the target, only the top pellets marking the paper. Most of them were at least a foot low. Lucky pigeons! Our good book explained that we had three possible problems: too little powder, too weak powder or too much shot. Through trial and error we decided the powder was too weak and the little house was reopened for use whilst we decided what to do. The book informed us that the best powder was made by mixing it up wet, the running together of the ingredients giving much better results. We poured water onto our remaining mix of gunpowder, stirred well and left it to dry.

The petty

Several days later the mixture hardly seemed to be any drier so we decided desperate actions were called for. Our kitchen had an old-fashioned coal-fired range for heating water and cooking. We spread some paper out on the oven shelf and covered it with our wet gunpowder, leaving the door open so that if it fired, at least the oven door would not be blown off. Now I am not sure if my mother knew what we were drying, but she never complained, so probably ignorance is bliss, as they say. We did not dry much at any one time, working on the theory that if such a small amount did catch fire but was not restricted by either the oven or house door, it would only burn. Fortunately, this theory was never tested because I reckon if the mixture had fired we would have been in for a redecoration job, perhaps with some building work as well.

We now found that the powder was much better but according to our book we were now blowing the middle out of our pattern of shot. We soon remedied this and when we next tried our cartridges we came back with a good bag of pigeons. Over the next few years the petty door became heavier and heavier – indeed, it must have been the heaviest door in the parish. Apart from causing us to be much more particular about cleaning our guns, the black powder served us well.

During this spring I undertook to plough two fields of grassland; by this time our outfit had turned over many acres of grass and I felt something of an expert. It is very satisfying to see the furrows leaving the mouldboard in unbroken lines, the grass turned under with well set skimmers. Absolute accuracy is demanded and it is a very happy tractor driver who can make a good finish with all the grass buried and yet leave it shallow enough for later cultivations to be made as easy as possible.

I was trying very hard to do a good job here because the field was seen from the road and I took a great deal of pride in my ploughing. The field also served as an advertising board to help bring in future work. The land over the hedge had just been taken over by the army who were using it as a vehicle storage depot. There were lines of army trucks and a few Austin utility pick-up vehicles regimented into place by the hedge across the other side of the field. The area was really parkland containing some trees and a hard-top road leading to a large house that had, until recently, been the home of our local vicar but had been empty until the army commandeered it.

The army personnel were billeted in the house but the control centre seemed to be a kind of mobile office placed over by the hedge. It was from here that a sergeant ran the operation. Access to the field was from the main London to Carlisle road. Both this and the entrance to the road across the field were obscured from the sergeant's view by a large oak tree. This meant he did not have a good view of any 'visiting' officer who might be inclined to visit without notice – the army people seemed quite touchy about the odd tin of petrol that found itself escaping out of the back door in exchange for a pheasant or a couple of rabbits. In view of this the sergeant must have decided that the tree would have to go. I remember him well – cropped hair with a round face, quite a pleasant chap to speak with but then I was not part of his squad. He must have had good contacts within the army because during the second day I was there a corporal and his squad arrived in an army truck with red-edged wings. This gave me the idea that they were something to do with explosives and I was expecting them to place devices under the oak tree and blow it up – I was wrong. Ladders were placed against the tree and the squad climbed up.

That night the tree began to look as if it was decorated for Christmas, with small parcels tied to it in many places. I left the tractor for a break and walked over to inspect. I was told that they were going to 'take the tree to pieces.' They were well equipped with diagrams and were obviously treating this as an exercise in explosive-setting techniques.

Nowadays one might be appalled at destroying such a fine tree, but in those days no one bothered very much. Leaving two soldiers to guard the explosives already set the squad promised to return the next day and finish the job. I ploughed on until dark. Next day the tree climbing act was gone over again and at about midday the corporal came over and asked me to stay at the other side of the field. The traffic on the road was stopped and two of the army personnel ran from the tree to the ditch with a reel of wire, letting out a cable behind them. A few seconds later all the charges went off, not with a mighty bang as I had been hoping but just a dull crump. The oak tree disappeared. Later I was told that where a charge was fastened to the tree on one side a counter charge was strapped opposite so there was a counter explosion which caused the wood to shatter. Indeed there was not a piece of tree left that could not be lifted by one man – it had completely disintegrated. I have never seen such a demolition job before or since, using explosives. I guess they must have used enough explosive to finish the war. Now the sergeant could see his officers coming from a distance so I guess he was happy.

During that summer I remember spending many hours mowing grass, also rolling the spring corn and doing odd jobs. We had lots of work now and the days were long. Often I would be out at 5 am and still tractoring as it went dark. In midsummer this would be as late as

11.30 pm – we had double summer time by now. As July approached we began to receive requests from our customers to cut their corn, usually wheat or oats, and I had to investigate procuring a binder. I found our trusty Warag would rent us one, so another £12 a year was spent. I remember very well fetching the machine from the depot. This was in Leaper Street, Derby, a journey of about six miles but it meant crossing the town. So Henry was driven across Derby, obstructing trolley buses and lorries as he went. But if it was a difficult journey there, the return was certainly much worse. First, there was the width of the binder to cope with, and to make matters worse it did not have a central towbar but one that was offset by about three feet, so every traffic bollard and light had to be navigated with extreme care. I was followed through the town by chaos: hooters blowing and drivers shouting. Luckily I could not hear them properly due to the noise of Henry, not just his engine but the iron front wheels clattering on the road, especially where there were cobblestones.

As we reached the traffic lights at the junction of Midland Road with London Road the lights changed to red and, of course, I stopped. Green came and off we moved, but the stop had caused us a problem. The governor came in with extra bite and, looking around I saw that a wheel had seized up – no one had thought to grease it. To make matters worse the axle carrying it had bent and the wheel was now catching the binder frame. I had to stop. The chaos was now worse than ever. The police arrived, surprisingly sympathetic I thought, and the binder was wound up off the ground until the wheel could be taken off. Water, obtained from a nearby shop, was poured onto it and when cool it was lubricated with oil. The wheel still caught on the frame, but with a spanner jammed in its

Albion Yeoman binder

holder we just managed to get home. No one asked to see the driver's licence that I did not have.

Now that the binder had arrived safely, it was time to put it together. During the war most machinery arrived in shipping condition and the customer had to put a great deal of it together himself. Our binder arrived with the canvases in a sack, and the reel or sails, the control levers, reel drive and main drive chain all in a crate. The PTO unit with all its fittings was also crated. The binder was probably allocated to us because few farmers had PTO options on their tractors. You will recall that we had already purchased a PTO drive unit to power our winch for the forest work and so we were able to use a PTO binder.

When assembled, our binder worked well – even the new knotter tied knots with reliability. Working in a wheat field, tractor running well, binder steadily turning out neatly tied sheaves of corn with a steady clack, clack,

clack, as the sheaves dropped to the ground from the discharge arms, our satisfaction reached heights we rarely experienced in wartime. The realisation came to us that this was indeed food for us all.

When you have ploughed, drilled and harvested a field of wheat at a time when you are constantly being told it all depends on you, or the nation starves, there is a wonderful sense of achievement to see all those sheaves lying in rows in the sunshine. Farmworkers, Land Girls, older schoolchildren and wives from the village all worked to stook up the harvest and make it safe before any rain could harm it, and there was indeed a marvellous fellowship in those wartime years. It has never been experienced since. The old slogan 'Churchill to lead us, Woolton to feed us', Woolton being our Food Minister at that time, really counted.

As the summer of 1942 closed and the harvest finished we looked forward to another winter of austerity, but we still had our memories of the good harvest. In our area the ground began to get wetter and Henry's steering showed definite signs of wear. In fact, it was so bad that when turning at the end of a furrow when ploughing, the front wheels leaned so much that it was necessary to stand up before they could be turned to the straight-ahead position. Whilst I was trying to move the wheels from full lock one day, there was a resounding crack and the steering lost resistance – the wheel just turned freely. The Fordson water air cleaner model, of which Henry was an example, had the steering gear enclosed in the rather large air cleaner, and in this case one of the end teeth had broken off the steering rack. From now on I was driven nearly insane trying to figure out ways to operate without turning to the right. If this could not be avoided then I tried not to allow full lock to be reached. This was particularly difficult in view of the severe wear on the steering pins etc. I found that if the wheel reached the position where the tooth was missing, then the only thing to do was to reverse and the wheels would come straight of their own accord, and the steering wheel would engage with the rack again.

After our refit on Henry he now looked more like this 1937 model. Note the notches on the radiator for blind adjustment, unique to this year's model

These problems could not be allowed to continue, but spares were hard to find. However, our local Ford dealer, Messrs Gillotts, came to the rescue and obtained a new air cleaner, steering box and clutch operating mechanism. This rather extensive repair meant that Henry was now updated to 1942 specification, at least as far as the steering and air cleaner were concerned. Pity the modern day

76

tractor restorer who has to figure out Henry's original specification, which was as registration number HNU 744. The total cost of the new parts was £25. I wish I could say that the update made a great difference to performance, but apart from an improvement in the steering it was a retrograde step – the engine never ran as well again.

Because the machinery we had on hire from the Warag was in nearly constant use and our output of work was higher than average, I was now on better terms with the field officer, Mr Wooliscroft, and decided that we should apply for a new tractor – a Fordson of course. The application was duly sent and acknowledged, but a warning was given that it might be as long as six months before a Fordson was available. It was good that I was now friendlier with the field officer, because in the spring of 1942 I had become old enough to serve in the Home Guard and found myself attending drilling practice with my wooden stave. We did not have enough rifles, so I suppose we would have been defending our village with pitchforks if the Germans had ever invaded. Because I worked at night and could not attend all the Home Guard evenings, I was always under threat of being reported to the courts by the sergeant, for avoiding duty. On the other hand, Mr Wooliscroft would have been most displeased to see me neglecting the food production job, so I just set them against one another and waited.

Now winter was here again, if I was not out working or attending Home Guard duty I was probably out duck shooting with Fred. We still had air raids, not as bad as earlier in the year, but annoying. With practice, I found it possible to ignore them and at least stay in bed at night, even though the air raid siren would usually wake me. Anyway, most of the bombers were more interested in the industrial areas than our rural one. Our duck shooting helped our meat rations along and the only thing we really lacked was heat. Our house had a coal fireplace, but coal was rationed, so we turned to the countryman's good old stand by – wood. We obtained a circular saw, a large open crank engine and a Bamford corn mill for £5. The saw gave us hopes of a warm Christmas, so we spent some time finding fallen trees we could cut up. My old boss, Mr Hollins, gave us rather a large specimen, about five feet in diameter. So one Sunday Fred and I called a wood day and set to work. Now, it was obvious our saw was nowhere big enough to face this size timber, even if we could have lifted it. So we set about driving wedges into the tree so we could split it into manageable pieces, but we soon found that this was very hard work. Fred and I never cared how long we worked, all night was not unusual if a vehicle had to be mended, but we both avoided hard physical work – I still do. Fred called a halt after about half an hour's graft. He decided we could use some of our gunpowder stock to help with the job.

The smaller branches were cut off until the trunk was bare of brash, and a one inch hole drilled about three-quarters of the way through the trunk. About half a pound of powder was poured into the hole and a piece of stiff card pushed in along with a length of our home-made fuse (saltpetre soaked string). Then the hole was filled with wet soil which was rammed really tight. We lit the fuse and retired some distance away. Nothing happened. After some time we went for a look. The fuse had gone out just on entrance to the tamped soil – short of oxygen we decided. Then I remembered that when I had seen the army blowing up a tree some time before they had used electric wire. Fred carefully removed the wet, tamped soil whilst I returned home for some wire and a motorcycle battery.

The wire I obtained was known as lighting flex and was made of two strands twisted together, opening up each strand we carefully removed most of the wire elements until only one from each wire was left. We twisted these together and buried them in the black powder and retired as far as the wire would allow. Luckily, this was about twenty yards, not far enough but it had to do. Touching the ends of the wire to the battery terminals produced an almighty bang – our fuse worked. Inspecting the tree afterwards we found it was not only split but also broken in two. We had used too much powder. With practice we found that less powder worked much better and also allowed us to split smaller pieces. We never had to use the wedges again.

I returned to the estate woodyard job with the tractor and winch, and this provided another source of wood to burn. So as Christmas approached we lived quite reasonably – much better than the unfortunate people in the towns still suffering from air raids and food shortages. This is not to say anyone was starving, but our rationing system left a hole in the stomach even though rations were calculated to provide just enough for a healthy body. In fact our nation as a whole was believed to be in better health under rationing because our diet was better balanced than previously.

As Christmas came nearer, I fretted about the new tractor on order and my mother fretted about what we would have for Christmas dinner. Fred and I decided that we should find something better than a cockerel and that the solution was already swimming about on our river. Yes, it was one of the king's birds (we did not suppose he would miss it). So we dined on swan, or to be more precise a cygnet. The new tractor showed no sign of coming, so after Christmas Henry had a valve and ring job, along with a new coat of paint. Even the paint caused problems as there was none in stock. 'Well try and get me some for collection on Friday,' I said. 'I will call on the way to market. I shall have a dozen eggs with me.' So Henry had his new coat of Fordson Green, courtesy of our hens.

7

IN the spring I obtained a contract to plough about 20 acres of land in a neighbouring parish, a district where I had not been before. It was nice land but a little undulating. Having ploughed about ten acres with no problems, I was happily following the furrow when there was an unusual noise and a cloud of dust billowed up by the furrow rear wheel. Looking over the right wing I found myself peering straight into a large hole – the ground had gone. As Henry plodded on, rear wheel running happily along the furrow bottom, soil disappeared alongside and the hole grew in size. I did not stop, figuring that if we were moving forward and not downward all was not lost. Clearing the area of the hole I dismounted from the tractor to inspect. The hole was about 15 feet across and possibly 40 feet deep, with a large amount of fresh soil at the bottom and it looked as if there had been rail tracks there at some time – a mine. I knew alabaster was mined at Chellaston, but had never thought unused workings presented any danger when ploughing. Later I realised that I had ploughed over all the land that had fallen into the mine shaft, and must have crossed it several times before it collapsed as I reached firm ground again. How lucky can you get? I finished the field but when ploughing through the low places I sat on the wing, just in case any more holes appeared, hoping that if they did I could jump clear. Maps were later found that showed the location of various mine workings, but no one knew if they were accurate.

During the winter we could relax a little from the

almost continuous grind of farming and food production. There was the local Agricultural Discussion Society one evening each month, also an occasional concert in our village hall and even a trip to the cinema, although one was always aware of the possibility of air raids. Once, in 1943 I think, we decided to visit our local cinema to see Charlie Chaplin in 'The Great Dictator'. Usually we could not use the car for such outings because the penalty for making non-essential journeys was quite severe. Farmers were a little less vulnerable to these restrictions, being able to visit other farmers on 'business'. The system was to telephone a friend and arrange a visit for the evening one wished to go to the cinema. The friend had to live beyond the cinema so that if one was stopped in a police check the destination would hold water. One could stop off during a journey if it did not increase the overall mileage. So on this particular night we set off to visit a farmer, to discuss producing better rations for milking cows from home-produced products, calling at the cinema on the way.

Our journey took us along the main road into our local town, Derby. This meant passing the railway works and sidings, which were protected from aircraft attacks by a smoke screen which was supposed to make them invisible. This smoke screen was composed of a crazy arrangement of oil burners each of which had a round base holding perhaps 10 gallons of some noxious fluid distantly related to oil. Each base had a five foot chimney topped by a 'hat' similar to a Chinese coolie hat – presumably this was to spread the smoke. These burners were placed about six feet apart, alongside any road that ran past a vital factory or similar place. I never knew if the screen was effective, but these burners certainly gave off the most poisonous fumes I have ever experienced.

Goodness knows what they burnt in them, but eyes streamed and breathing was very difficult when one was in proximity to those roads which were 'protected'. How it was possible to justify the burning of so much oil when it was brought into the country from overseas and had to

Salamander oil burner

run the gauntlet of the submarine blockade, and the great loss of life associated with it, I will never know and what it was that fuelled these burners it is difficult to say – probably a mixture of oil and tar. In any case, it took many people to clean and refill the burners each morning.

We drove through this foul foggy mixture, on this particular evening, to visit our farmer friend, calling at the Gaumont cinema in Derby to see the film on the way. It was topical at the time – a send up of our enemy, Hitler – and we enjoyed it very much. When I saw it again a few years ago, I found it dated and not a very good production, but it certainly helped morale at a time of difficulty and trouble.

During this winter Terry and I worked hard, both on the equipment and in the woods, clearing brush ready for replanting. In March a letter from the Warag arrived telling us we could have a new tractor: a Fordson would not be available for two years, but we could have a David Brown in May.

This caused great excitement – new tractors were few and far between in those days and to obtain a permit to purchase one of the few allocated to the home market was quite an achievement in itself and had originally meant filling in a form and producing a strong case for justifying the use of a new tractor. Desire to own and use came low on the Warag priority list. Some time before, Charlie had been granted a permit and had been allocated a Fordson which was even fitted with rubber tyres. This was almost unheard of. When the Fordson came we were all surprised at its paint finish – desert sand with camouflage markings. It had obviously been destined for the desert and then diverted to the home market. It really did run well compared to poor old Henry. I well remember the first time it rained on the tractor and dull sand-coloured paint ran down the side of the radiator on to the ground. Such was the quality of our wartime paint.

Having been allocated a David Brown, I thought it time to find out something about the make. A neighbour had one but we were not well impressed with it as it looked rather small. A visit to our local distributor produced a leaflet and this whetted our appetite a little more. The leaflet was well produced and gave us information we had never known before. We could not get a permit to purchase rubber tyres for it but found we could buy rims, and I decided it was possible to fit Henry's tyres on to them. The main problem seemed to be the price: Fordson, including rubber tyres, was £225 but David Brown on spade lugs was £299 – quite a substantial amount more. However, we decided that since Henry needed a fair amount of money spent on him we would be much better off with the David Brown. The decision was made – the tractor would be ready to collect in the second week in May. We arranged for the Ministry of Transport to allocate our lorry a load to Huddersfield, where the David Brown factory was, so that we could collect the new tractor. I was disappointed to find it painted in army drab grey, not the bright red shown on all the publicity hand-outs. But the paint was well applied and seemed much better than that on Charlie's new Fordson. We were shown round the factory and eventually departed for home with our new toy.

Perhaps we should delve into history a little here, as not everyone knows that David Brown made the first Ferguson tractors. Harry Ferguson had, of course, been developing his tractor with the concept of perfect balance, light weight and hydraulic control of the implements over many years, and finally must have decided it was ready to present to the farming community. It was due to be produced in Sheffield, I believe, by a steel company. However, for some reason, perhaps lack of funds, space, commitment or just a disagreement with Ferguson, it was cancelled and David Brown, a leading gear-cutter looking for diversification, finally produced the first Ferguson tractor. These Model A tractors were available in 1936 but never sold well. This was partly because farmers did not grasp what a move forward the Ferguson hydraulic system was, and partly because the tractor was too light to be able to utilise the 'drag' implements on the farm. Another problem was the lack of a PTO facility.

After about two years' production the David Brown factory was beginning to choke up with unsold Fergusons, and David Brown himself was pressurising Harry Ferguson to move more tractors, clearly stating his opinion that the existing tractor was too light, lacked wheel width adjustment and had no PTO facility. In the end David Brown produced a tractor design which cured all these problems, but in the meantime Harry Ferguson had visited America and shaken hands with Henry Ford on a deal to produce the Ferguson System tractor in the USA. This was the catalyst that made David Brown produce his own tractor, incorporating a little more weight so it could haul the Fordson type 'drag' implements. It also featured four forward speeds, against the Ferguson three, a PTO facility and a new four cylinder OHV or overhead valve (OH – valve in head) engine, with much increased power. The down side to this was that the Ferguson patents meant that David Brown could not use the Ferguson hydraulic system or the converging linkage layout for attaching the mounted implements. Therefore, the new tractor had to use straight up and down hydraulics and non-converging linkage. Our new tractor was equipped thus, and it proved a good buy over the 15 years that we kept it.

About this time in May 1943, my life was getting very hectic: another harvest was approaching and the Home Guard was putting more pressure on me to learn to use a rifle and also to throw hand grenades, as well as all the usual rifle drill. The autumn ploughing programme was not far off, with its quota of night work, a lot of machinery wanted repairing for neighbours as well as ourselves, and I had bought a motorbike. It was not really a motorbike but an Auto Cycle – this was a bicycle with a small engine fixed under the pedal area. It had a beefed-up frame and wheels. The engine capacity was 98cc and was a single cylinder two-stroke. The bike also had a cork clutch and single speed gear unit, and was made by a company in London named Raynal. One of the local farm workers had decided to seek employment elsewhere, and sold this very placid machine to me for £5. It was only two years old so it was quite a good buy. I used it to fetch and carry small parts and even for pleasure, as far as the law would allow. But it soon proved very disappointing, particularly to my pride. Pedalling uphill and also to start it, left me open to much derision, particularly from Fred who had at one time owned a Scott 600cc motorcycle. All this hassle soon had me looking for more power and speed. Many parts were discarded: pedals, heavy mudguards, carrier and of course the silencer. The engine was stripped and piston rings renewed and at the same time the cylinder ports were enlarged and polished. Considerable research went into the gas flow in the cylinder, which had a flat-top piston. Gasses were supposed to collide within the cylinder and thus force the exhaust out, with the resulting part-vacuum helping to suck the incoming mixture into the cylinder. I figured out a way to modify the cylinder ports, that would allow the gas to exit faster, thus sucking more mixture in so the next charge would be as strong as possible. A light and short exhaust pipe replaced the silencer. A push-start was now required to get the bike going. This proved okay, but I had to sprint like a stag to get the gas flow moving fast enough to produce powered motion. Having mastered this, I found top speed increased from about 30mph to 45mph, and the noise was incredible.

8

RETURNING to the subject of the engine, circular saw and the corn-mill, I feel it is worth recounting the opportunity that led to us purchasing them. At the beginning of this story I mentioned the farm sale where the same engine was sold to the incoming farmer for 12s 6d. Several years later we were looking for an engine to drive a corn-mill, for my father and I now grew corn on the small farm which we had been able to rent. Much to my surprise, when I was doing a ploughing job on the farm where the sale had been held, I found that the old engine was still there.

I asked the farmer what he wanted for it and this brought forth much chin-scratching, a match to light a fag and the words: 'Yowd best lewk at it fust.' Moving a pile of rotting old sacks and numerous thatch pegs, I uncovered the engine in its dank dark alcove in front of the cows. I couldn't see much and so decided to return with a torch the next day.

The torch revealed an open crank engine of unknown parentage: hopper cooled with a horizontal cylinder, brass carburettor and three foot diameter flywheels. The carburettor had a curved brass air-intake with a venturi section about halfway up and a variable jet situated just above the venturi. The fuel came direct to the variable jet via a pipe from a fuel tank situated under the horizontal cylinder. Turning the flywheels proved the engine was not stuck, but it only turned about half a revolution before it stopped dead. Half a revolution in the opposite direction ended in the same dead stop.

One only had to look at the cylinder block to see that it had considerable frost damage. The bottom of the water jacket and part of the side had been blown out and lay on the floor underneath the engine. This was obviously a big repair job.

About a year before I inspected the engine a scrap man had offered 10s for it, but because the cows were in the next shed the farmer told him to come back next day when the cows were out and the thumping and banging of his sledgehammer would not disturb them as he pounded the engine to pieces. The man never returned and I bought the engine for £1, the saw bench and Bamford corn-mill for £2 each.

Moving the three items took all day, but in the process I found that the engine turned over quite easily when the brick that had fallen out of the wall was removed from the crankcase and no longer fouled the big end as it revolved. With this crumb of comfort I took the engine home. Being young and more impetuous than I am now (I think), I decided to see if it would go, the reasoning being that if it would, it might be worth trying to repair the frost damage.

As the engine's two flywheels were resting on the ground and it obviously could not be started like that, we placed it on two railway sleepers and drove nails through the bolt holes in the engine base, securing it to the railway sleepers beneath. The points on the 'flick' magneto were cleaned. We stood a tin of petrol alongside the engine and connected it to the variable jet with a rubber tube, squirted oil around liberally and then began to turn with the short starting handle. Thirty minutes later the only visible result was two human figures prostrate on the ground gasping for breath, petrol and oil running liberally about the yard.

Gradually recovering from our exertions, and studying the engine, we suddenly realised there was nothing to cause the inlet valve to open. The exhaust valve was blessed with a pushrod, but the inlet was totally naked. It then dawned upon us that it must be suction operated, and it was stuck. More oil and careful use of the hammer freed the valve and the old engine burst into life, or perhaps I should say 'exploded' – the railway sleepers were not fastened down so the outfit wandered about the concrete like a noisy free-range hen looking for worms, and by the way it hammered and pounded the concrete I bet the worms underneath packed their bags and fled.

We now decided the engine was good enough to try and repair, so it was laid on its side, the broken casting cleaned, and straw and many years of sediment were removed from the water jacket. We could then see that there was a strengthening rib around the cylinder. This was drilled and tapped in two places and we had the broken casting back in place. Various suggestions were made to stop the water leaking from the casting – filling the bottom of the hopper with cement was one. But finally I obtained some 'stag' steam jointing, and after applying this liberally, screwed the broken piece in place and left it for several days to set – it never leaked again.

Having repaired the engine, we decided to use it for grinding corn for the cows. Our old mill had been driven by the tractor and in any case was way past its best, so in a rush of enthusiasm we built a new shed (corrugated iron) to house our recently acquired grinding outfit. The saw bench was used for sawing the wood we managed to split and I have the resulting scars on two fingers, but the two fingers are still with me and they work quite well! When the shed was finished it was time to bed down the engine and mill. Having seen the engine exercising its free will on

An engine similar to the one we used to drive the corn-mill

the concrete, we knew it would need a sturdy concrete bed to tame it. A deep hole was dug in the shed floor and old iron pipes and metal were driven deep into the ground to reinforce the concrete. A four-sided box constructed without top or bottom was laid over the hole and the engine placed on top resting on two horizontals of wood. Two cwt of cement was mixed four to one with sand, old brick ends and stones. This mixture was poured into the hole and up inside our box until it was about two inches from the top. Bolts were suspended through the engine-mounting holes and into the concrete mixture which was left to set. Next day we took the engine off and filled the two inches remaining at the top of the box with very sloppy cement. There were no stones, etc, in this sloppy mixture because we needed it to run level for the engine to sit on. It settled quite level and when hard was ready to receive the engine. The bolts stuck up enough to hold the engine and, of course, were in the right place to fit the mounting holes in the engine casting.

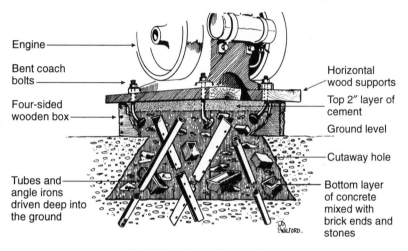

Bedding down the engine

The mill received similar treatment, but this time it was necessary to line up the pulleys with string to ensure the belt ran true. When all was set hard a belt was cut and joined. Our grinding outfit was ready to produce ground oats, or so we thought. But the first snag came to light as soon as the engine was started – the mill was running backwards. You know it is always the simple things in life that cause the trouble. However, after some thought we realised the belt must now run crossed to reverse the direction the mill rotated. We hoped that we would now be able to grind corn as the animals were rapidly running out of feed – 30 cows and 300 hens were innocently eating their way through our dwindling stocks without a care in the world. Our troubles were only just beginning.

Bags of oats were brought into our new grinding shed and set out by the mill. A gallon tin of petrol was filled and connected to the jet with a rubber tube, and oil was supplied to the parts we thought needed it. Oats were poured into the hopper, the engine started and we were off. The oats came out of the hopper through a hole in the bottom, which fed a trough running down to the rotating plates that did the actual grinding. There was a lever on the side of the trough that controlled the angle and would obviously allow more or less oats to flow down the trough. Alas, no oats could be persuaded to run down to the plates unless we fed them by hand. Then we noticed a cam on the main drive shaft, close to the trough. It must be meant to vibrate the trough and cause the oats to run down easily. We eventually bolted a piece of flat strip to the bottom of the trough to make contact with the cam and cause the trough to vibrate. Even then the oats did not flow easily. This was cured by a piece of old inner tube being stretched to hold the strip against the cam. The job was up and running. Henceforth, this arrangement was referred to as 'the bloody wobulator'.

The engine was running well, the mill screamed its head off and oats continued to run into the plates, which were screwed together until the right type of flour was produced. Ten minutes later we had only about half a bucket of ground oats. We had to do something better than this if the animals were to eat: it seemed they might eat at a faster rate than we were currently grinding. More thought brought us to the conclusion that the mill was not running fast enough. The pulley on the mill was not very big so using a smaller one would not give a big enough boost to the speed. Luckily, we found the main shaft on the mill was long enough to allow the pulley to be slid across in line with the engine flywheel, but would this be too much for the engine? We could only try it.

More time passed, but eventually the rusted pulley was moved, the belt reworked yet again and the outfit re-started – and how it went. The engine no longer went *bang-suck*, it just went *BANG* all the time. The mill screamed at an even higher pitch, which kind of collided inside your head, and could still be heard an hour after the outfit had been stopped. Of course, we had no silencer on the engine and the open exhaust was inside the shed. But we were grinding half a ton per hour and the animals' future seemed much more secure. Eventually the exhaust was extended so it blew outside the shed. Unfortunately, one of Mother's roses grew in line with the pipe, so she was now the proud possessor of a black rose, probably the only one in England. Strangely enough, the rose grew there for several years before she moved it, the fumes and smoke never killed it.

With the outfit now working to a reasonable capacity, we found it a full-time job to satisfy its lust for work. We had to carry oats, constantly change bags on the mill, refill the hopper and keep the engine well-lubricated. The big end was lubricated by squirting oil at it with a force-feed oilcan, as it went past. This resulted in a fine oily mist and a well-lubricated shed roof. Water was quite a problem – the engine constantly boiled, so we had to fill the hopper at frequent intervals. But worst of all was the fuel problem. The original tank was full of holes so we were managing with a one gallon can. This worked well until it was half-empty: at this level the engine would not pull the fuel up to the valve, so when it started to misfire we stood the can on a brick kept for the job. We soon found the engine ran just as well on tractor fuel and this meant an oilcan for starting and a petrol can to run on, so we were constantly juggling cans around. The challenge was never to stop the engine. If the can started off at too high a level then the engine would choke and not run cleanly. At one stage this almost led to disaster.

The incident happened in the early days of our grinding experience. I had filled the petrol tin and stood it on the brick. Wrong again: it did not need to be lifted when full. Just as the engine was ready to start I realised the piston had not had its oiler filled, so putting down the starting handle I filled the oiler. Now, normally we started the engine by one person swinging it whilst the other held down the inlet valve. When enough motion was generated and as the inlet valve was released, a free hand was held over the air inlet as a form of choke, and off the engine would go. Being a Derbyshire man and 'strong ith arm & wick ith yed', I evolved an alternative system where a rag was stuffed into the air intake, and the flywheels rotated backwards until compression was felt. Then, with an almighty effort, the handle was accelerated as quickly as possible and the engine would go over compression. Next time the engine was turned it would fire – a quick dive to pull out the rag would be necessary – and it would gradually pick up revs and go. Unfortunately, on this occasion I had forgotten to pull the pipe out of the fuel can, so fuel was gently percolating into the air intake and soaking the rag whilst I oiled the engine. The almighty swing followed and much to my surprise the engine did not go, but on the third revolution spit back into the air intake. A sheet of flame shot across the shed, led by an inflamed rag, distributing fire over sacks of oats and general rubbish we had by now accumulated. Petrol was burning around the air inlet, on the mounting block, running around the tin of petrol and threatening to fire the surplus oil from our crude oiling system.

My instinct was to run, but I then realised it was not as bad as it seemed. So I decided to remove the petrol can before it also went up in flames. In my excitement I forgot the pipe leading from the can to the engine, and grabbing the can made off towards the door only to have it snatched from my hand by the resistance of the pipe. The can hit the floor and a sheet of flame hit the ceiling, curling off towards the door. I went with it; so smoke, flame and I emerged into fresh air together. Then I remembered the new fire extinguisher a high-pressure salesman had persuaded my father to buy only a few days before, against my will I may add. So I grabbed this derided piece of equipment and pointed it at the fire, which was extinguished at once.

The barn engine explodes into life

Those were wonderful days: noise, warmth from the engine, the smell of hot oil and the 'all go' action of carrying oats, water, fuel and corn and of trying to keep the shed tidy.

9

WE had used our new David Brown tractor for about two weeks, mostly for mowing grass. It was June and the English hay harvest was just beginning. The pneumatic tyres removed from the Fordson had been replaced by spade lugs and poor Henry had been sold to a local public works contractor where I suspected, after all his faithful service to us, he would meet a bad end. Three years' continuous grind and many memories had passed since he was purchased. Now he was sold for £40 more than we had paid for him. The 11.25″ × 24″ tyres were fitted to the David Brown wheel rims, and five-hole Ford lorry wheels were fitted to the front hubs. So now we had a tractor with four pneumatic tyres for the first time. Our first two weeks with David proved very disappointing: the light work of grass cutting seemed to cause spark plugs to oil up as if he had an oil well in the sump and I almost wore out a wire brush cleaning them. The tractor also had very high oil consumption.

Despite the fact that it was wartime and all sorts of labour problems existed, if we had any problem with Henry we knew we could rely on advice, and if necessary, a visit from Gillotts, our local Ford dealer. We did get advice from our David Brown dealers in Derby, but very little else, and even that was mostly wrong. We could never inspire enough urgency in them to visit us. They were, of course, truck dealers, who only had tractors on sufferance, or so it seemed to us. It was obvious that they were terribly short of staff to meet the demands of the truck repairs, many of which carried various priorities from the ministries, who seemed to issue priority repair schedules like confetti, whilst our problems came way down the list. However, after a somewhat abusive visit to the workshop, the dealers suggested that the cylinder walls might have been badly finished when new and so had worn out the piston rings. We were invited to take the tractor in to them for replacement rings. When the work was finished we found the limitations of wartime warranties: the piston rings were free, but gaskets and labour had to be paid for. Furthermore, we could not have our tractor back until the bill was paid. Our new tractor had made a bad start and the David Brown dealers a worse one.

The tractor went back to work and oiled just as many plugs as ever. Some weeks later, after many desperate calls to David Brown, we were notified that a representative would call on us and give advice. He duly came, and without any hesitation took off the valve cover, turned the rocker shaft until 10 spots of oil per minute dripped from each rocker arm, in place of the 30 or so which had previously dripped, and David didn't oil a plug up for weeks. Later, when I had a tractor repair shop, I was able to apply this knowledge to other tractors and everyone thought I was a genius. Some hope! Fred had looked on these trials and tribulations with interest, but was unable to help. When told of the cure, he became fond of quoting from the Fordson instruction book to the effect that the Fordson oiling system was entirely automatic, requiring neither oil pump nor pressure.

By the time David had settled down, the 1943 harvest was fast approaching. There was no other job on the farm that gave me greater pleasure than cutting corn, wheat in particular, with its hard straight straw. This was especially so now that the fields first ploughed a few years ago were producing good crops and clean straw with no grass or weeds in it. It was bliss to drive a quiet-running tractor and hear the clack of the binder discharge arms, as sheaf after sheaf of good wheat fell in straight lines on the ground for the following gang to set into stooks. The stooks turned away any rain that might fall during the time the grain must stay in the field, hardening. In our district the stooks traditionally had to hear the church bells ring thrice before they would be ready for the stack.

Cutting corn was the one job where I needed an assistant to work the binder. Terry, still at school, could only be there a small part of the time. So, as I travelled from farm to farm, I had a different binder operator on each. This was a far from satisfactory situation. Naturally, the farmer held back his best and strongest workers for stooking, and I had either a part-time worker or, more likely, a member of the Womans Land Army. Now if you think spending days in the sunny harvest fields with an often not unattractive young lady could be something to savour, you could be correct. But bear in mind I was under pressure to finish quickly and pass on to pastures new, so there was no time to dally. Also, these young ladies were forced, in many cases, to work on the land or join the fighting forces, a choice disagreeable on either hand. Also, they often had little interest in what they were doing, especially if previously they had been working in an office, all nice and cosy, and could return home after work and perhaps meet a boyfriend. I was in the habit of working until 11 pm and expected my helpers to stay as long as I did. In addition, I almost had to train each one to operate the binder individually. If it was not operated well, a lot of time could be lost correcting mistakes. Of course, before I receive a barrage of complaints from Land Girls who feel they did much better than I have described, the ones who had volunteered to join had a good record of working skills and of devotion to farming, whilst many of those forced to work on farms became interested in the work and as they did so, their value to agriculture and the country grew considerably. Indeed, some married into the countryside and are still with us today – older and wiser.

The problem of the binder was solved for me in a rather unexpected way. My father's uncle came to visit one day, and hearing my complaints volunteered to 'ride binder'. 'After all,' he said, 'I did have a settler's half section in Canada, and had to bind all my wheat.' He returned to England in 1925, but believe me he had not forgotten how to keep the binder reel at the right height to lay the corn on the canvas, and was always sure to keep the twine at the right place on the sheaf and listen to the machinery working and stop the outfit if he felt something was going wrong. From then on our output increased quite markedly.

The winter of 1943 was just as awkward as the previous ones: labour, spare parts and fuel shortages were getting worse than ever, but we were not quite so pressurised with work. This was undoubtedly due to a better supply of tractors gradually becoming available so our customers were slowly becoming more independent. I suppose it was from this date that our cultivation business started to turn into a repair operation. Something took place during this winter that I shall never, indeed cannot, forget. My old boss asked my father to take the truck and collect the furniture and effects of a new man he had persuaded to come and work on the farm. The truck arrived back loaded up with household effects and people. I did not know at the time, but my future wife had arrived in our village.

By this time the Battle of the Atlantic was drawing to a close. Without our ships crossing the Atlantic we would probably have lost the war. Churchill certainly realised this and although he inspired us with his speeches he and others must have known so much better than we did how close we came to starvation of population and to closures of factories. Hitler certainly knew how vital our link across the Atlantic was. His fleets of submarines came very close to winning this battle. How many people now remember the hundreds of ships and thousands of men lost each year in the cold waters of the North Atlantic? How terrible to cross the water in lightly armed or even unarmed ships, in rough weather when the cold winter sea gave anyone forced to leave ship and enter the water a life expectancy of only minutes. Even worse for the tanker crews particularly those carrying petrol: one torpedo or bomb and the ship could erupt into a fireball, roasting any one near. Perhaps even those in the icy water could consider themselves better off. Naval escorts did sterling work, particularly in the later stages of the war when submarine detection devices became more accurate – so much so that at the end of the war a German submariner's life expectancy was only 60 days. How terrible to be sealed in a submarine damaged beyond repair and incapable of surfacing, knowing your death in this icy chamber was only minutes or, even worse a few days away.

We as land workers were aware of the sacrifices the sailors were making, perhaps not so much then as we are now, for censorship of the news was very strict. So when you are at a tractor show and see a round sticker on a tractor tank, in blue and yellow, with the words 'We won't waste it, sailor', just think for a moment of those far off days and the people who have never seen the last 50 or so years because they made the ultimate sacrifice so long ago.

With the slackening of work I now came under more pressure to attend Home Guard duties. In these new circumstances they became much more enjoyable and a nice change from working every evening. I had an army uniform with brass buttons to polish, boots to keep clean and a rifle, although we were not allowed to have ammunition. How like the British, that in 1940, when invasion looked a certainty, we had only wooden staves and pitchforks to defend our country, but now the invasion seemed unlikely we had guns and hand grenades. The grenades gave me much amusement. Fred and I had become used to explosives (our own), but many of the country men who formed the Home Guard were not used to them and were in some awe of them. However, we practised with dummy ones and had it pushed into us how dangerous they could be. I suppose in my 'know all' youth and full of confidence I did not realise how frightened an older person, with more responsibilities than I, could be when handling these lethal weapons – also how inept our organisation was.

The day came when we were to throw our first live grenade. We were taken to a rifle range where a trench had been dug, World War One type. I reckoned even after three years of mobile war our upper brass were still fighting the first World War in the trenches, so we had a trench with spoil banked up on the 'enemy' side of it. Our sergeant, quite a capable chap, started off by throwing the first one. The resulting explosion from over the bank did nothing for our anxiety. So here we were a set of country lads ready to go to war, with our first explosives. We all had a go. I threw mine left hand forward, right arm back clutching the grenade with the pin out, in what I must admit was a sweaty palm. A strong throw sent it over the spoil bank whilst everyone else ducked down in the trench. So we all took our turn until we came to a rather timid lad who maybe was a little slow on the uptake. No doubt excellent at calving a cow, he was visibly nervous with explosives. He went through the motions, just as he had been taught, but failed to clear the bank and the grenade rolled back into the trench. A crisp command from our sergeant to clear the trench was quite unnecessary – we were gone. Some digging was required to repair the trench, but our village contingent survived unscathed.

As the dark nights came upon us we put great effort into rigging lights on to David Brown. This meant various visits to the car breaker. New parts were not easily obtainable and in any case were very expensive. Used parts were cheap and plentiful due to the fact that cars were not much used and thus the demand for spares from the breaker was low. With lights on the tractor I could now work better at night and what was more important could travel home on the tractor when necessary, to save our petrol ration – although, if the truth be told I was not too keen on night work with lights as I felt it made me a sitting target for the enemy aircraft that still came over: one felt very vulnerable sitting in a field lit up like a Christmas tree.

One of the times I felt at risk from the enemy, indeed was at risk, was during this time working with lights. I was aware that enemy aircraft were overhead because the searchlights were arcing across the sky. So I turned the tractor lights off. There was some anti-aircraft fire and a few flashes in the sky from exploding shells. I continued to plough on, partly because I could still distinguish the difference between the light stubble and the dark ploughed ground, also the field was large and flat with no cover other than the ditch at the end of the furrow. I was making for this place of relative safety when there was a terrible bang which frightened me beyond description – then silence, other than the engine noise as David ploughed on. I later found a hole the size of a tea cup, with awful jagged edges, where a piece of shrapnel had gone straight through the tin scuttle that gave an element of weather protection to the driver. The scuttle can be easily seen on early pictures of David Brown tractors. The thing that puzzled me was that the hole was at the side of the fuel tank and just above my knees – how I still have knees, albeit a little stiff these days, I shall never know.

The slow journeys home on our tractor soon induced me to look for more speed. Fred and I, aided by Terry, decided an auxiliary hand throttle, that would override the governor was needed. To this end, we tied a piece of string to the throttle rod and whilst I steered David, Terry pulled the string. Fred followed behind in his Austin 7, to check the speed. We reached 28 mph but could easily out-accelerate the Austin on sharp corners. A hand throttle was quickly made from an old handbrake lever, so journeys home were much quicker and definitely more exciting. Funnily enough, the engine never seemed to suffer from this abuse.

Our Crossley car was by now definitely getting worse for wear and during the visits to the car breaker I had seen another Crossley parked in his yard. It was the same age as ours, but a sports saloon with better lines. I managed to do a deal for this car and got it for £10. Terry and I towed it home with David Brown. Some parts were used to fix up the old car for a while, but eventually, as the war finished, I rebuilt the sports saloon and it became our full-time car. These Crossley cars had Bendix brakes, cable operated, with a complicated system of self-energising brake shoes.

My first mechanical vehicle—a frightening thing with no brakes. Mother and Grandmother look on in 1929

A David Brown tractor similar to the one we received

An early Fisher Humphries plough taking part in a ploughing match in 1944

Betty and I at Blackpool in 1946, in the Crossley car before the rebuild (above left), and (right) the Crossley car after the rebuild, seen approaching Ambaston village through flood water in 1946

The day after the incident on the Scott. The bike has had its carburettor and gear lever restored and I am in working order again. Note the white sock on my right foot, which is still sore

David Brown on emergency flood delivery in Ambaston village 1947

My father and David Brown—I can just hear the sheaves rattling out of the binder

Here I am driving a Fordson model F at a steam rally many years later

This gave me many sleepless nights, as I did not understand the basic principle but had to learn it as I went along. I found that if the springs retaining the shoes were not placed correctly the brakes varied from lethal to non-existent. Even replacing one spring in the wrong position could alter the brakes so when the pedal was touched all wheels instantly locked. Or if another variation of the springs was tried the brakes worked quite progressively going forward, but the car could not be held at rest on a hill. Another variation gave wonderful brakes in reverse but none when going forwards.

Luckily, our sports saloon gave us an emergency brake. This was provided, unintentionally, by the manufacturer, who had equipped this car with a four-speed Wilson epicyclic gearbox. The engine could be idling quite happily whilst the small gear lever on the steering column was in a gear engaged position – usually 1st. When one desired to move forward the clutch pedal was pressed and then released, just as a normal clutch. When moving forward in 1st gear, 2nd was selected on the steering column mounted gear lever. When 2nd gear was required it was only necessary to press and release the clutch quickly and 2nd was engaged without removing the hands from the steering wheel, and so on through the gear range. It was quite impossible to miss a gear and the emergency brake I mentioned could be provided by engaging 1st or even reverse once the car was rolling along in top gear. A quick press of the clutch pedal allowed this selected gear to be engaged and the clutch feathered in to provide a brake. I expect the instruction book would have warned not to do this or severe damage to the transmission would be caused, but we did not have an instruction book and our transmission never gave any trouble at all. Luckily, after a few weeks trying, I found out how to set up the brakes correctly and we did not need our emergency brake.

During this winter I became enthused by Fred's talk of big motorcycles. He had once owned a Scott TT replica Flying Squirrel. This was a twin cylinder two-stroke of 596cc capacity. I tried to find one, but it proved impossible. However, I had the idea of asking our dustman to keep his eye open in case one was hiding in a back yard somewhere. He then said, 'Why not buy my old Matchless?' So I did, for £8, complete with sidecar. This machine was of 1000cc capacity, with a side valve V twin engine. We soon took off the sidecar and tried the bike up and down our lane. Oh, the power after the Auto Cycle. It was fantastic. The wheelbase was rather long for solo riding but I soon got used to the way it would squirm and snake if it was pushed around a corner too quickly. But on the straight it really was wonderful. This bike raised problems for Bruce, our spaniel, because apart from duck shooting his great love was to go with me on the tractor, especially now we had a David Brown and he could share the double seat. He always looked to go with me but could not figure out a place to ride on the Matchless. This was solved by putting a sack bag over the tank and lifting him on to it. He would sit there, basically sitting on my knee but with his front feet on the tank, between my arms – he loved it and soon it was difficult to go without him. His ears would fly out in the wind, his snout point forward. His face might be battered by rain or encrusted in snow – it made no difference, he just had to go and he kept the worst of the weather off me. Spaniels seem to make good motorcyclists. I had a cocker spaniel some years after Bruce and he was the same. They both leaned quite naturally into the corners and would sit still when we were under way. Some other dogs I have tried panic when cornering and lean the wrong way or try to abandon ship at speed, but not Bruce. He soon learned to be an 80mph spaniel.

1944 was the year our well-used Bedford truck left and a new one took its place. A permit to buy was obtained and, for the sum of £544, a new three ton, flat-front Bedford took up residence in our yard. The dustbin job had by now been given up and Father spent all his time on haulage work. I was working more and more in our small workshop looking after the local farmers' tractors, many of which were David Browns. There were of course many Fordsons as well. Our business was flourishing. Very little was heard of income tax, or rules and regulations and we were able to concentrate on work. If we made profit, apart from our modest living requirements, we could spend it to make our business better. Looking back, it was wonderful not to have the hassle of PAYE or VAT and act as the government's unpaid tax collector, or be almost inundated with forms to complete.

There was still a reasonable amount of tractor work to do, but this increasingly became more and more seasonal – mostly harvest and autumn ploughing. But now we usually got the worst land to plough, the customer ploughing the easy going, so we charged more money per acre than previously. I still ploughed during the autumn nights, but now there seemed no threat from enemy bombers. Indeed, one of the pleasures on a moonlit night was to stop the engine a moment and just listen to the muted roar of our planes setting off to bomb our enemy. We were not close to bomber airfields, but if you put up 500 or even 1000 planes for a night raid they inevitably spread over a wide area. It was now easy to see Churchill's threat of three years previously when he said: 'We shall reply tenfold,' coming true. This speech was given as we received the first of the Blitz in 1940/41.

10

AT about this time Fred and I began to think of the time when Bruce would no longer be able to retrieve ducks off the river. We decided a replacement would have to be obtained and put on stand-by to take over from our old friend when the time came for him to retire. Fred looked around during his travels and found a young, black cocker spaniel bitch – Bessie Dog had arrived. She proved to be very excitable, making a great deal too much noise for our duck shooting trips. But we hoped she might calm down in later life and in any case prove a suitable match for Bruce. Later, when Bessie was about two years old, Fred arrived one morning to see if Bruce was available for 'special duty' – he was. He then stayed at Fred's house for two days after which he returned home. But it took some time before he paid as much attention to retrieving ducks as he paid to Bessie. The novelty eventually wore off and some time later Bessie provided a selection of replacement gun dogs. Fred kept a black pup whilst I chose a liver coloured one with a white front paw. When they were weaned our pup named Rex came to live at home with Bruce who took to him surprisingly well, though even now I can see the pained expression in his eyes as the pup jumped all over him: a 'What have I done to deserve this?' expression. Fred never gave his pup a name, just calling her 'pup'. However, whilst working on a farm he made contact with an American serviceman who wanted a gun dog. He came to see the prospective animal and asking its name and being told it was 'pup', repeated the name which then came out as 'paap' in his American voice. This name stuck and left us to holler 'paap' across the countryside when we were calling our new gun dog in later times.

Sadly, my pup met an unfortunate end. We had just got used to him and found a growing attachment to his character when he went missing one day. We searched long and hard but found no trace of him until we noticed the wooden top over the well in our garden was broken, sure enough there was Rex in the water at the bottom, swimming strongly in circles where he must have been for about two hours. A true water dog, he must have inherited his father's water ability. The sad ending to this was that about four weeks later he developed a skin problem whereby he started to shed his coat and break out in sores. This spread to Bruce almost before we knew it and after several weeks of treatment by our vet we were forced to accept the reality of the situation − both dogs would have to be put down. We mourned many days for our two friends but never knew if the experience of Rex in the well, or if perhaps Bruce picking up an infection in the river had been the real reason for our loss. We felt that probably the well was the cause, but after all we had been drinking the water until two or three years previously. A sad day.

It seemed very lonely on the tractor without Bruce. In addition, Terry was now using another tractor my father had bought − a Fordson on steel wheels and the International plough which we had previously hired from the Warag and had now bought off them. I had a new Fisher Humphrey trailed plough, with the same Ace bottoms as the International but many different features. About this time our local ploughing society − West Hallam and district − decided to revive their annual ploughing match which had been suspended from the outbreak of war. So now we had a new interest – the beginning of a hobby I still participate in even today. We did not see it as a hobby in those days but as an opportunity to show off our skill and perhaps attract some new customers. Neither Terry or I had ever seen a ploughing match, but when the day arrived we were keen and hopes were high. Luckily we both won our respective classes, returning home with award cards tied to the front of our tractors.

During this year the wartime gloom began to lift – it was becoming clear we were likely to win. England seemed full of Americans and we could only marvel at their smart, fine-material uniforms, whilst ours were coarse cloth. They were also well-equipped with wonderful six wheel drive trucks and of course jeeps, the like of which we had never seen. These soon took their place on all the pub car parks and the dance halls. Apart from the support and help we were now getting from the Americans, the presence of this wonderful band of happy carefree people lifted all our spirits – that is to say all of us except the fathers who had daughters being escorted by Americans. This caused many difficulties at the time, but looking back I expect most of the problems now seem of little importance. Once again our two nations were becoming entwined in history, to our mutual advantage I feel sure.

With the better war news the future was looking brighter. I was spending more time at home in the workshop, doing repairs for our neighbours and had noticed a pretty girl cycling off to work each day. 1945 came and victory seemed just around the corner, although it also seemed an uncommon long time in arriving; but come it did and our local paper was full of plans for peace celebrations in Derby, our local town. VE Day (Victory in Europe) eventually came and victory was announced. In the evening I decided to go to town and see what was happening – there was no way any work was being done. So kicking the Matchless into life, down our lane I went, only to meet the nice girl and her mother walking back up the lane, having visited Derby to take in the sights. A spur of the moment decision made me stop to talk and enquire if there were celebrations in town, indeed there were so the pretty girl, Betty, was invited to climb aboard and share the visit to town. I got the feeling Mother was not entirely happy about this unexpected turn of events, but she gracefully agreed, so now I had a girl on the motorcycle in place of Bruce, or Terry, who had a girl-friend in the next village and, no doubt, was celebrating victory as well.

Derby was an amazing sight: streetlights lit, shop windows ablaze and hundreds of people just walking around hand in hand spread across the streets singing the popular songs of the moment and some of the favourite war songs. People from the army, air force, and some sailors, even here a hundred miles from the sea, milled through the streets. There were some Americans but not many, as the majority we had been seeing over the past months were now in France and Germany. The ones we still saw were certainly celebrating. I wondered if they were thinking of other Americans still desperately struggling on beaches in the Pacific, or wondering if their time to travel halfway across the world and return to fighting and bloodshed would soon come along. We hoped blackouts were now a thing of the past, hopefully forever. Five long years and at last it was over, at least in Europe – what a wonderful feeling; I shall never forget it. So Betty and I have no problem recalling the day we met. The Matchless became our key to freedom as we pushed our parents into giving us more freedom for time and travel together, although this was to some extent curtailed by the plentiful supply of work available and the limited supply of money this provided.

After this inspiring few days, life went on as usual. We still needed food, spare parts, fuel etc and many things were still rationed, but we got on with our work and watched the progress of the war in the Pacific developing in our favour. When the terrible events in Nagasaki and Hiroshima brought the war to a conclusion we had another great celebration. But looking back after all these years I wonder whether we were justified in celebrating so much death; however, we had suffered our share and war had brought a stronger belief in the philosophy of an eye for an eye.

Terry and I, now having girlfriends to consider, decided the old sidecar must be resurrected and fitted back on the Matchless. Considerable thought went into this project. The original fixings were complex and difficult to undo, so we decided the sidecar must have fittings that could be removed easily so it could be ridden solo as often as possible. We achieved this by the use of a ¾ inch bar threaded with a coarse thread, which was all our limited resources could muster. But home-made fittings never gave us any trouble. The sidecar was another matter. The old-fashioned body had rotted during its rest over the war years, so we built another, not elegant but functional. It had a flat board bottom, rounded front and an old Austin 7 seat recovered from the car breaker. This was fastened well back, to leave plenty of legroom, so our new partners could sit in line – alas, I cannot say 'in comfort'. Nevertheless, the four of us had some wonderful times together on this outfit. Parking in the countryside we would pair off, one couple to the left and the other to the right, arranging to meet back at a certain time and in the meantime free to do our own thing.

I had soon mastered the art of cornering on three wheels and found that the exuberance of youth taught me to drive with the sidecar wheel off the road, even with the girls in the sidecar. This was quite an achievement since the outfit was so big and heavy. Right-hand corners were easy, but left ones quite difficult without dropping the wheel. The girls soon learned to hold the sidecar wheel to prevent it from revolving as we travelled for miles without it contacting the road.

As time went on the tractor work kept getting less and less whilst the repairs began to pile up. I had seen an advertisement in the farming papers for rebuilt Fordson engines available from Webb and Waite in Stretford, Manchester and after contacting them I decided to purchase one. I bought a battered Fordson shell and added the engine to it, hoping a rebuilt tractor to sell would improve our finances. The wonderful Case, International Harvester and Allis etc. tractors were now getting very scarce indeed. I wondered how many of these tractors lay unused at the bottom of the Atlantic. It was sad to think of these things, but I hoped this scarcity might be to my advantage at least. My battered Fordson came into the workshop and was stripped and cleaned. Anything needing fixing was dealt with and the whole tractor repainted. But before I could advertise it, a neighbouring farmer fell in love with it and payed me £70 for it. From this time on I almost always had a much-used Fordson around, just waiting to be face-lifted. The engines I collected from Manchester proved to be excellent units and well worth the £25 I paid for them and soon a market developed which was difficult to meet. Sometimes for week after week I would take a Fordson into the workshop on

Sunday and clean it and take it to pieces, always renewing the seal between the engine and gearbox and fitting new clutch plates. On Monday the engine would be loaded into our car trailer, for the journey to Manchester which was made on Tuesday. On Wednesday and Thursday I would fit the engine and complete any other repairs needed. The tractor would be painted on the Friday and delivered to a waiting customer on Saturday. We would bring his old tractor back, ready to start again on Sunday. The price we asked soon rose to £100 per tractor and this gave me the best income I had ever had.

Often I worked until the early hours of the morning, so my social life was a bit limited, but Betty and I managed to meet several times during the week and we gradually became closer. True to form, the ladies' influence both on me and Terry began to weigh upon us with demands to go to dances and film shows. Now, I could not dance a step and Terry was not much better, so we were persuaded to enrol for dancing lessons in Derby. It soon became obvious that 'dance dressed girls' were totally unsuited to the sidecar and in any case it played hell with hairdos. We got limited relief from this problem by nailing an old blanket to the rear of the sidecar and when the girls were seated this was brought forward over their heads and tucked into the front of the sidecar nose. Of course the girls could not see where they were going, but at least it kept the worst of the wind and frost off them. The journey to Derby was about six miles and we found that a certain canal bridge, with a speed limit of 30 mph I may add, could be taken at 60 mph when a condition of near zero gravity could be achieved. Now, the girls could not see the approach of the bridge and so as we breasted the rise, screams could be clearly heard from the sidecar. We never learned to dance a step, but

116

enjoyed the experience of trying.

My father had had a new flat-fronted Bedford lorry, army type, for about a year by now. The bin emptying job was long gone and he filled his time with general haulage, mostly for the corn trade. However, an opportunity came along for him to rent a small farm, so the Bedford was sold and he became a farmer. Of course, we had plenty of machinery to run a small farm with and only the livestock needed buying. Ten milk cows and a horse eventually arrived. My father, who had originally been a horseman or wagonner on a farm, loved horses and no doubt felt this was his chance to own one. Captain, as the horse was called, came to the farm late in life, probably fourteen or fifteen years old, but we needed him not to do the heavy work which could be done with David Brown but to make my father independent and able to take feed out to the stock, or do any light job without the need to stop the tractor doing its contract work. Captain became a great favourite of my mother's – she would feed him titbits over the gate at the front of his box. I never knew what 'make' he was but there was a distinct yellowish tinge to his coat with some darker markings – as soon as he arrived I christened him 'the yeller oss' and the name stuck. He lived in a loosebox across from the house. I suppose an estate agent would describe it as desirable stable with corrugated roof, antique hayrack, good manger, newly whitewashed with good views over muck heap. Anyway, Captain liked it and was soon at home there. He could see everyone who came to the farm and he tended to snicker at them to make sure they had not forgotten to bring him a titbit. He was quite a character and tended to go desperately lame if anyone other than my father took him to work. A few coarse words and a slash over the rump would soon get him going again in the realisation that his ploy had failed.

Cows – well I hate the things, thinking of them as dirty and stupid. Have you ever seen one with enough intelligence to be trained to perform in a circus? Anyway, my father milked 10 or 12, twice each day and seemed to enjoy it. My mother had hens and ducks running loose in the orchard. The ducks soon found a way down to the brook which ran for about 200 yards. Off they would go, waddling away across the home field line astern, each morning. Later, Mother would go looking for them and collect any eggs that had been laid on the bank. There she would find them, riding at anchor like a flotilla of warships or greedily sieving the muddy bottom for all kinds of unmentionable things which were however, edible for ducks.

Nationwide the food situation was getting worse than it had been in the war. I felt this was partly due to the politicians again looking to party politics and the fact that the population was loosing some of the 'all pull together' spirit we had during the war years. In the main we were poverty stricken as a country, and could ill-afford all the things needed to rebuild, and eat at the same time. The lack of foreign funds meant I could still sell rebuilt tractors easily – new ones were not coming in and English production was needed for export to buy the many things we could not produce ourselves.

During this post-war period, as already stated, we felt worse off both financially and materially than during the war, but our personal food situation was made better because we were now farmers and were allowed to kill two pigs each year for our own consumption. We took full advantage of this regulation, but it was not easy to take a rather appealing baby pig; feed it for six months or so and then watch it killed and catch its blood in a bucket, for making black pudding; scald the body with boiling water to make the removal of the top skin and bristles easy, then cut it up and salt the main part for bacon. However, we soon lost the sad feeling when we were eating the pork and looking forward to having bacon for breakfast in the near future.

By this time the country was running out of motorcars. Our Crossley was getting long in the tooth. Its doors had dropped, and its rear end and the front above the windscreen were rotting away. So I decided to replace some of the affected parts. The car, of course, had an old coachbuilt body which was mainly of wood. I felt I could replace the pieces of wood causing the trouble and during a snowy period of the winter of 1947 I started the job. Well, if you have ever seen a cat chasing its tail you will know how I felt. As soon as one bit of the body was taken off it exposed another that was just as rotten. To cut a long story short, the body of rotting wood and corroded aluminium panels, was completely removed and I started to make a new one. The front wings, made of steel, and the bonnet were the only usable bits. Now, I would never claim to be a 'body builder' but needs must. However, a full-size, four-door body was beyond even my bigheaded confidence; so an open two-seater was decided upon. Careful measuring and the use of imagination soon told me the chassis was too long for this type of body. So I sawed it in two and removed 18 inches from it, along with the same amount from the drive shaft. This was rejoined using a piece of tubing that was a tight fit inside the original, and the chassis was plated inside and out and held with ⅜ inch bolts – no welding as we did not have the equipment. Although the car did a lot of towing in future years nothing ever came loose. In spite of this it probably would have failed its MOT test in today's red tape-ridden world. The rather short body was built and seats made. Mother sewed up a hood, in black canvas, to fit the frame I made from the wooden laths from binder canvases, and we had a motorcar again. I learned a great deal from this experience. Some original ideas went into the body, such as a safe to keep valuables in and a fold-down back to the seat – this was to prove invaluable as a courting couch in the not too distant future. With the new body so much lighter than the old one, top gear performance and mileage per gallon were tremendously improved and apart from a somewhat squarish look the finished motor was not too bad.

Our local David Brown dealer seemed more independent than ever now and spare parts were much more difficult to obtain. However, we found that a dealer at Newark – Newark Tractors – had good stocks, so we ceased to trade in Derby and turned our attention to Newark. This suited me because I enjoyed the sixty or so mile trip to the town to collect stock. One occasion I remember was a visit to Newark on the Matchless motorcycle. As I was returning, in the direction of Nottingham, an air force man thumbed a lift and since he gave me the sign (he must have been desperate) I stopped and picked him up. The road between Newark and Nottingham had many stretches along which the old Matchie could be driven at speed. The machine never had a speedometer, so I can only guess the maximum we hit was about 80 mph. Rolling on towards Nottingham, with the twist grip pulled well back, the machine started to misfire and before I knew what was happening there was a shriek of tortured rubber and the engine had seized. We snaked around a bit and eventually I managed to pull to a halt. The air force man said, 'What was that?' 'Well,' I said, 'you may as well try for another lift. This bike ain't going any place yet.'

I had visions of finding a telephone and calling for a tow, but after allowing time for the bike to cool I tried kicking it over — the engine was free but would not turn a full revolution. I sat and thought for a moment and the idea came to me that the problem must be the rear cylinder because that one would be running the hottest of the two, having less air flow than the front one. I also deduced that the problem was probably something to do with the aluminium piston. It seemed logical to remove the rear cylinder head (I think the Americans call them L heads), and as it was a side valve this was not difficult. With the head removed the problem was plain to see — there was a lot of aluminium dust, a broken piece of piston and a ring of metal loose in the cylinder. Now the problem could be seen it did not seem so bad. Obviously no walking would be involved, which was good as it was totally against my 'religion'. Taking the broken bit of the piston out of the cylinder, I found that it had come off just above the piston pin, so the bottom half of the piston was still fastened to the connecting rod and could now go up and down normally when the engine was turned, albeit with a whooshing noise reminiscent of a steam engine with asthma. An attempt at starting the old machine soon produced life and I had a single cylinder motorcycle instead of a twin. This, indeed, was progress even if there was a fairly intense spray of oil coming out of the rear cylinder. When I put the head back on, the oil spray ceased and I was able to ride the bike home, at reduced speed of course.

The Matchless remained in this condition for some time as it was not possible to find replacement pistons for it. However, eventually Fred and I found that Bedford lorry pistons would fit, so two cast iron pistons took the place of the aluminium ones. This, of course, put the

121

engine out of balance and we did our own balancing job, but the Matchless was never the same again and efforts to locate a Scott motorcycle were redoubled. Eventually one was found – a 1928 three-speed Super Squirrel in very bad condition, but it only cost £5. With considerable help from Fred, the Scott was rebuilt and the Matchless sold.

11

ABOUT this time life began to change considerably for
me. In truth it changed for everyone in Britain.
Betty and I were becoming closer, Terry left our employment and went away to do his own thing and eventually
to serve his compulsory time in the army, Fred and I,
whilst still good friends, spent less time together, mainly
due to my attention to Betty and we now had a
Socialist government which was very anxious to bring in
nationalisation and free health provision. Whilst I per-
sonally greatly regretted the fall of Churchill and the rise
of Socialism, it is true to say that Socialism never gave me
any problems – neither did it do me any good in the long
term. If one door was closed by the politicians taking
away some perk or advantage I had become used to, it was
only to be expected that another would be sought and
found. Even the steep rise in health provision costs was
met without undue difficulty, by either working a little
longer or increasing the amount I charged for some
service I provided. It is interesting to note that the new
National Health Service increased my health provision
costs by about 300%, but this was not regretted if it helped
the country at large. I accepted that many people, as my
granny constantly told me, were much worse off than I.
The disillusion set in when one heard people saying,
'Have you had your new spectacles yet? I got some today,
quite free. Yes, I know I can see OK. But they do not cost
anything so I might as well have them,' or 'Oh yes, I am
quite well. But I went to the doctor with my back and he
gave me a week off work, so I can draw sick pay – my

wife wanted me to decorate the bedroom.' Such were the advantages of the welfare state we were beginning to experience and in my opinion these were the beginnings of the 'English disease' as it later became known, when we were constantly whittling away at our prosperity, with wildcat strikes and other industrial diseases. I am not being ultra political: things like this just made me laugh since it was obvious the people perpetrating these foolish actions were robbing themselves most of all, though that is not to say they were not, to some extent, also robbing me and others.

Our old blacksmith had retired and a new one came on the scene. He was a talkative man and more of a general metalworker than farrier. I found him easy to get along with and spent many happy hours working in his shop, hoping to learn more about metals and heat. One day he told me he owned a tractor – a Wallis. This wetted my curiosity and I was directed to look at it. I found it in a barn, but was unable to start it. After an examination, finding the front wheels leaning inwards, the spade lugs on the rear wheels well worn, half a turn play on the steering wheel and the governor rods and controls desperately worn, I came to the conclusion that it was better left in the barn. However, a few weeks later we obtained a new pair of rear tyres for our David Brown. The old ones we had taken off Henry Ford and used for the David Brown were, by this time, worn out but the casings were sound. My blacksmith friend expressed an interest in them so we did a swap: he had a pair of worn-out tyres and I had a worn-out tractor.

After some work I got the tractor running again. So when we were busy my father would drive David Brown and I, our latest toy. The old Wallis was in fact, or had been, a wonderful tractor. I had repaired the front axle and managed to adjust some of the wear out of the steering box. The governor was hopeless but a hand throttle was improvised and this worked well, partly due to the long-stroke, low-revving engine. We never used the Wallis for ploughing but all cultivation work suited it very well. I had many happy days just sitting on the seat, going back and forth with a set of disc harrows or a cultivator, whilst the Wallis just ran at about 1000 rpm all day in top gear. It did everything in top gear, which was the perfect gear for our operation. It also had a hand clutch, three-speed gate change gearbox and a water injection system for assisting combustion – this did indeed make a big difference and was probably why the engine was flexible enough to work in top gear all the time. 'Massey Harris' was written across the radiator and 'Wallis' vertically up each rear wing. The old tractor did good service until, one day, a big end failed. I always intended to do a good repair job on it but, like many things, this was never done and in the end the tractor was cut up for scrap. What a pity.

Our Scott motorcycle was now the transport mainstay for Betty and me. We did not use the car too often because the fuel required was considerably more than the Scott used, so it was decreed that we must brave all weathers, although we did use the car on particularly foul days.

The TT motorcycle races in the Isle off Man now began to feature in my plans. Before the war I had always visited Donnington Park races. Indeed, my memories of this venue go back to when the track was surfaced with loose gravel and spectators walked alongside the track whilst the motorcycles were passing. I can remember how terrified I was by the speed of the bikes and the sound of their open exhausts which almost blew my ears out. There were very few meetings that I missed before the war, so it follows that I had knowledge of the TT Races, although I had never visited the Isle of Man.

Fred was a regular attender before the war and thus he and I decided to visit the post war TT as soon as we could. The Scott carried us to Liverpool and, for a small fee, was parked in a garage near the pier head and we set out on foot for the boat, to cross to the island. I remember queuing for hours to get on the boat and arriving in Douglas about 7 am. We had breakfast in Douglas and then took a coach trip around the course. Now, for those who are not familiar with the course, it stretches for 37¾ miles around the island on public roads which are closed for the purpose. We left the coach at Kate's Cottage, about six miles from Douglas, with the idea of walking back to town during the race. For me the most devastating thing was the first rider to pass us as we sat on the stone wall just down from Kate's Cottage. The bike travelled at over 100 mph, the bumpy road causing severe snaking as the machine leaned over. It passed within five feet of us, descending the hill towards Creg ni Bar hotel about half a mile away. The noise brought back those days of Donnington Park, in the early thirties. But, of course, this was so much faster. I have since been to this race many times but I have never forgotten the very first rider who nearly blew me off that stone wall so long ago.

I have so many memories of these races. Later Betty and I visited for the whole week and well remember some of those wonderful sunny and warm days – perhaps they are all remembered like that when you are in love. These were also tragic days. We knew how dangerous the Isle of Man course was and how many victims it had claimed – truly an adults' course. On one occasion we saw a rider get into terrible trouble and wobble desperately at well over the 100 mph mark, mount the footpath and, as we people sitting on the wall dived over backwards, regain a modicum of control. He must have decided the worst was over and, still probably travelling at 70 or 80 mph, he dived back on to the road, when we think the front wheel collapsed, catapulting him into a telegraph pole which he broke in two. The bike took the pole off near the ground. There was dead silence for a second, then screaming people and running first-aid men, who dashed to the pole. One of these men was the hotel keeper with whom we were staying. He realised that one of the poor rider's legs lay on the road whilst the rest of him and the bike had gone over the wall into the field behind. Afterwards, he said: 'I looked in shock at this leather clad leg and on the spur of the moment lifted it up, and threw it over the wall into the field, out of sight of the spectators.'

In spite of this fatality we visited the races for many more years until my other commitments did not allow me to go. There are many good memories, like having Manx kippers for tea on the boat as we returned to Liverpool on a glasslike sea. At other times the sea was so rough that, as we sat in a tea lounge, some of the chairs broke loose and we ended the crossing fending off chairs and the people sitting in them, with our feet. The teacups and pots were systematically destroyed through falling on to the floor and much to our amusement, a large tea urn was shot off the counter by a specially big wave, its contents spilling over the floor. We reckoned at least half a barrowload of tea leaves came out of it, leading us to speculate whether that was the total allowance for the summer sailings.

Our new project of the farm meant there was always something to do and one of the jobs was to repair the farmyard and various gateways around the fields. For this we needed a cheap surface material – ash. This we found at our local power generating station. So on spare days David Brown was to be seen with our trailer, made from the old Bedford lorry, the one we first owned and which had emptied so many bins in the beginning, setting off for the power station about four miles away. We soon made friends with the ash tip man – he who drove the little Lister narrow-gauge locomotive with its small trucks rocking along behind. He allowed us to use the Chaseside loading shovel, a Fordson tractor based machine with winch-operated cable system for lifting and tipping the loading bucket. We found that if we could start it we could use it, and when the choice was between starting the Chaseside or using a shovel, we found we could start anything!

Although David Brown was a relatively light tractor, it was surprising what he could pull – we reckoned about three tons of ash and one ton of trailer. The journey home was relatively flat but had just one gradient, which meant a gear change down to third gear. Changing up was quite simple, one just had to use maximum revs in third and shut the throttle, then double declutch while gently feeling for the gear teeth to mesh, but it had to be done slowly and then it usually went in like a knife into butter. If it was done fast people half a mile away might say: 'Sounds like Arthur missed that one.' Changing down was easier because usually the tractor began to struggle on top gear and lose revs. When enough black smoke was seen coming out of the exhaust pipe and the revs were just above idle speed, with the throttle fully open, a quick press of the clutch and at the same time a slam of the gear lever into third would give a quick, quiet change. The governor would lift the revs as the load was suddenly released.

This system will work for most tractors not fitted with synchromesh gears, but the speed of moving the gear lever will vary from one make to another, according to how far apart the gear ratios are. With my wicked sense of humour, I can now visualise drivers trying this method and not getting the revs and speed right. I can just see the chips of hardened steel flying around in the gearboxes, but rest assured, if you get it right it will work, but only on a hard, rolling surface.

It was about this time I had my most serious mishap on a bike – I do not say 'accident' because there are very few accidents. These things are mostly caused by carelessness or lack of observation. I had experienced two such things before this time, so I will recount them in case they might spur someone to take better care of themselves than I have in the past. The first one was whilst riding a Royal Enfield motorcycle which I had purchased from Betty's father – a 350cc valve-in-head motor, but without much clout from the back wheel. Following a car through a village and as usual exceeding the speed limit, I failed to notice he was giving a right hand signal. I was travelling quite fast and positioned myself to pass him as we breasted a rise and was waiting until I could see that the road was clear. He was concerned about making his turn and had not seen me coming up fast behind him. He turned just as I saw his signal. There was nowhere for me to go, so I trusted the theory that if you lock the rear wheel and give a good kick to the road, the bike will lay down on the side on which the kick is delivered – it worked and I found myself sliding along the road behind the bike. Luckily, the driver stopped and the bike and I slid across the front of the car. I can still see the end of the fender rapidly approaching my head, just missing impaling me by a few inches. In fact, even to this day, I believe it is possibly an instinctive move of my head saved me from serious injury.

On another occasion, a friend asked me to help him repair his 500cc motorcycle. It needed a rebore and a new piston fitting. This was quickly accomplished by getting the work done at a local garage that specialised in tuning MG sports cars. We thought this was a good place to get quality work done – it was in fact too good. Our repair man obviously had not allowed for the difference in expansion between water cooled and air cooled engines and in spite of running very easily for over 1000 miles the bike was still prone to lock up when hot. I took the cylinder and piston back to the mechanic with a request to increase the clearance and ease off the piston. He was horrified but with some persuasion he did this. My friend ran the bike again and it did not lock up, but he was unhappy with it and did not have the confidence to try it at full throttle So when it had done another 500 or so miles we decided this must now be put to the test. So he left it with me for the weekend and I decided to try it out on a local disused aerodrome runway. This is now part of the East Midlands Airport, but at that time was often used by people to have a 'blind' with their cars or bikes.

It was a miserable morning so I was wearing my heavy coat. Having sped up and down the runway six or seven times without any problems and gradually increased speed until I could travel the mile and a half at 75 mph, I decided the time had come to try it at full throttle. Hammering down the runway on full chat the speedo registering 85 and gaining, the bike suddenly locked up. I did not have time to blink before I was sliding after the bike on my back and feeling the joins in the concrete squares, like punches delivered hard. I was bruised for a week but rode the bike home and got some more taken off the piston.

The most serious incident happened when I was on the Scott. I was due to see Betty in the evening and first had to repair the oil tank under the seat. So I took off the seat, did the repair and without time to refit the seat rode off on the pillion. On an 's' bend down our lane I met a car – nothing unusual about that you say, but there is when both vehicles are on the same side of the road. The car's windscreen was shattered in the collision and the door pillar was broken (by my shoulder), half the front mudguard was torn off and so was my boot – lacerated as if it had been cut with a knife. The Scott retired to the roadside ditch without its gear lever or carburettor. I remember waking up in the ambulance – I knew it was a Bedford by the gear whine. After an X-ray of my shoulder and foot I was sent home with just bruises. My foot was only sore but my shoulder was black and dead.

The smaller fields on the farm added to a situation that suggested we should buy a mounted plough for David Brown, in place of the Fisher Humphries trailer plough we were currently using. Also, the added bonus of being able to move from farm to farm and indeed travel further to compete in ploughing matches, without dragging a trailer around, all helped us to make this decision. So a new David Brown plough arrived and I was able to compete in more matches, often leaving home as soon as it was light and not returning until it was dark, usually with a prize even if it was not first prize. At this time, of course, the classes were general purpose, semi-digger or long-board and this meant competing against trailed ploughs, as well as some very good mounted plough competitors. Never easy, is it.

As 1948 came along Betty and I decided this was the

year we must get married, but money was a problem and where would we live? Not with in-laws, we both said. I looked at finding a farm mechanic's position on a large farm, but in truth jobs were not so easy to find. Even in those days, however, we were saving money by not going to places of entertainment so much, but often visiting relations and friends. We usually went in the sporty Crossley – after all we had a courting couch in it, so were able to spend more time together in comfort (that is all I will say on that subject). In the spring Fred came up with the solution to our financial problem. He told me Alfa Laval were looking for more milking machine fitters. This was a job I rather fancied because on various occasions I had gone along with Fred, just for the ride, when he was working near home and realised I could do the job easily. Besides, I never tired of travel and the job seemed to provide plenty of that. Some money we had, some I made by selling various pieces of equipment and with a loan from my father we purchased a new caravan, taking delivery just before our December wedding.

My father bought a used Citroën car – a 1936 12/4, Rosalie was its model I think – and we inherited the Crossley to pull our caravan. Now, unusual things always seem to be happening to me, perhaps my odd character breeds them, but surely the problem at our wedding could not be laid at my door. The wedding day was 11 December, at St Chad's Church. I was there with Frank, my cousin, and Betty was on her way, resplendent in white and no doubt somewhat nervous. This was made much worse when the vicar told us the church register had not arrived and he must put the service back awhile. Eventually the register was located as being in the care of the churchwarden – and he had gone out for the day. There was a high power meeting all round and the vicar agreed to marry us straight away, it being arranged that we would sign the register the next week. Amazing how things go adrift. Even on our way to the honeymoon destination we were stopped by the police looking for robbers who had stolen the historic 'Stone of Scone' from the Palace of Westminster. The police wished to inspect the inside of our car, but seeing the bits of confetti falling out, they remarked: 'We can see you are not interested in the Stone of Scone, so carry on.'

Our new life provided us with a reasonable standard of living. Alfa Laval paid me £3 10s per week, with bonus payments according to how many pipe joints were made each week and a special payment for starting up a newly installed machine. They also payed 3½d per mile for the Crossley car to carry tools etc. My board was always paid by the farmer whose machine I was installing and I had to make special arrangements with him to cover this, due to our living in a caravan. But I found the farmers welcomed this and were willing to pay the £1 10s per week I asked.

Starting new machines gave me some of the most exciting times I ever had during my employment with Alfa Laval. Once the machine was assembled the same ritual was followed from farm to farm. First the units were completely unpacked, then the farmer, or whoever was going to use the machine, was instructed in its preparation and cleaning. When the time came to use the machine for the first time, it would be me who ventured between the cows with the shiny ticking bucket, to apply it. In those days, of course, it was unusual to sell a milking parlour, so all the ones I fitted were installed in traditional cowsheds which meant one carried these new-fangled things up between the cows. I made a point of asking the farmer to give a little extra feed whilst I was milking. This occupied the cow and gave me a good guide as to her reaction to the machine. If she stopped eating and turned to look at the new bucket, I would beware of a sudden kick. Even worse, if the cow in the other half of the standing looked, she was likely to hit you from behind and how strong cows are. All very exciting. Usually, the younger ones took to the machine much better than the 'old grannies' and in any case they were lighter and easier to control – control in my book meant pushing one's shoulder into the cow just in front of the rear leg and if you felt a muscle twitch, whilst feeding the machine on to the teats, simply pushing like hell with the shoulder so that if she was going to kick, as soon as a foot was lifted you pushed her off balance and she had to put it down again.

One grannie resented the new device so much she evolved a method of getting at me all of her own – both legs went up at once, the bucket was hit hard and bits of tubing, shiny new bits of metal and even milk flew all over the shed, and me. The first time this happened I unconsciously screwed my toes up inside my boot and her foot came down right on the toe, squashing it flat. So whilst the farmer searched for bits of milking machine around the shed I sat on a bale and used a fork handle to push out the boot toe. After that the farmer screwed up her tail, holding it upright and at every flinch he just screwed harder and lifted higher whilst I gingerly applied the machine again – a little heart-stopping, but one must never give the animal the idea that you are afraid or it will make her worse.

On one farm where I went to start a machine, it had been fitted by another fitter, there was a large shed, quite new, with a rather loud, shouting ex-army man as cowman, looking after about eighty cows. I guess the cows must have been used to him – ours would have run a mile. As he gave them instructions in full voice – 'Get you in there' or 'Damn you for a screw' – it was all rush and bustle with plenty of noise; just what, in my opinion, cows do not need if one is to obtain the maximum yield. All went well in the start up except that one youngish cow kicked with energy. Our cowman soon cured that: removing the tube connecting the unit to the pipeline he proceeded to thrash the unfortunate animal around the rear end and flanks, until it stood shivering. It never kicked again, but neither did it release any more milk, so quite apart from the obvious cruelty involved the exercise was totally counter-productive.

On going to one farm, milking about thirty cows, I was taken quietly to one side and told how good their milk production record was and that they had never ever had milk returned by the dairy because of bad quality. This I believed until it came to washing up instruction time, when we had to wash the milking equipment in the cattle trough in the yard, from which the cows drank. I found that other farmers used the dairy for storing honeycombs – the smell of bad honey could be really overpowering – and one used it for plucking chickens, a bucket of chicken offal lived in there all the time I worked on that farm. I instructed farmers to use a strip cup to draw off the first squirts of milk, to check for lumpy milk or signs of disease and then found that many never bothered to do this. Little wonder I have never drunk liquid milk since those days and certainly never will.

Now that Betty and I were settled in our new life we were enjoying the freedom and responsibility very much. We were having a wonderful time travelling from farm to farm with our caravan, especially in the winter when we were warm and cosy in our little house and the hours I could work were restricted to those when the cows were out of the sheds for exercise. In midwinter I was probably working no more than five or six hours a day. However, we did have to adapt to our new situation: I was now an employee and not my own boss for the first time in nearly 10 years. Would it work? Had I been spoilt by my ten years of lording it over my own business and staff of one – me! Could I adapt to being tied to a big corporation – Alfa Laval? These questions remained to be answered in the future.

Farming Press

Below is a sample of the wide range of agricultural and veterinary books and videos published by Farming Press. For more information or for a free illustrated catalogue of all our publications please contact:

**Farming Press Books & Videos, Wharfedale Road,
Ipswich IP1 4LG, United Kingdom
Telephone (0473) 241122   Fax (0473) 240501**

Books

Tractors at Work: A Pictorial Review 1904–1994
Stuart Gibbard

A highly illustrated book showing the working history of tractors in Britain and emphasising the uses to which tractors were put.

Tractors since 1889   Michael Williams

An overview of the main developments in farm tractors from their stationary steam engine origins to the potential for satellite navigation. Colour and black-and-white illustrations.

Farm Welding   Andrew Pearce

A fully illustrated guide to stick welding, gas welding and cutting, MIG/MAG techniques, soldering and basic blacksmithing.

Farm Machinery   Brian Bell

Gives a sound introduction to a wide range of tractors and farm equipment, incorporating over 150 photographs.

Videos

The Massey-Ferguson Story   Michael Williams

From the early days of Wallis and the General Purpose tractor right through to modern high-spec models.

Fordson: the story of a tractor

Featuring the five main Fordson models from 1917 to the 1950s, this combines archive material with new film.

John Deere Two-cylinder Tractors, Vols One & Two
Michael Williams

Volume One gives a vivid portrayal of the early days from the Froelich replica to the Model G. Volume Two continues with the later development of two-cylinder tractors from the new styling to the 1960s.

Farming Press Books & Videos is part of the Morgan-Grampian Farming Press Group which publishes a range of farming magazines: Arable Farming, Dairy Farmer, Farming News, Pig Farming, What's New in Farming. *For a specimen copy of any of these please contact the address above.*